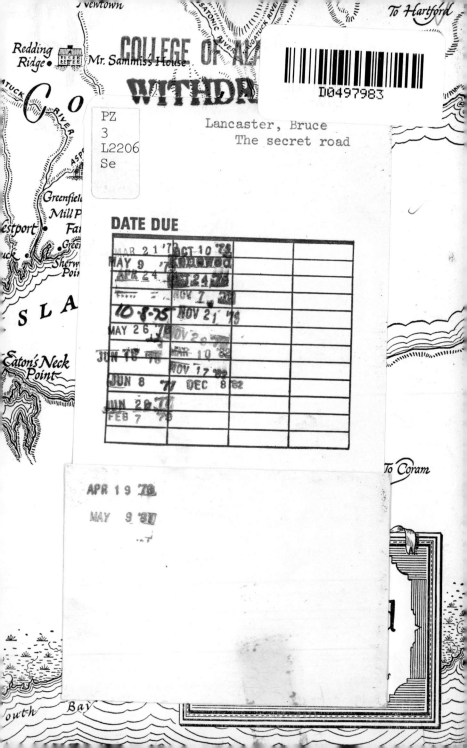

THE SECRET ROAD

The SECRET ROAD

BY BRUCE LANCASTER

AN ATLANTIC MONTHLY PRESS BOOK

LITTLE, BROWN AND COMPANY · BOSTON

ATLANTIC—LITTLE, BROWN BOOKS
ARE PUBLISHED BY
LITTLE, BROWN AND COMPANY
IN ASSOCIATION WITH
THE ATLANTIC MONTHLY PRESS

*Published simultaneously
in Canada by McClelland and Stewart Limited*

PRINTED IN THE UNITED STATES OF AMERICA

FOREWORD

Before the summer of 1778, General George Washington had no organized Secret Service. What information he had came from patrols, scouts, the interrogation of prisoners, deserters and refugees. With the growing need for sure and constant knowledge of the intent of the British Headquarters in Manhattan, he set up a sort of G–2 and OSS, having found reliable people for this work. Until recently, little was known of this service, which functioned quite smoothly up to the end of the war. The researches of the late Carl Van Doren and Morton Pennypacker have thrown much light on this subject; on those researches, chiefly Mr. Pennypacker's, this book is based.

Robert Townsend (or "Samuel Culper") was an actual person and, so far as the past may be reconstructed, operated much as is set forth here. A trusted merchant and society editor for James Rivington's *Gazette,* he went everywhere, knew everyone, saw much and heard much, sending his findings to General Washington. (Mr. Pennypacker makes a most interesting suggestion that the supposed Tory, Rivington, may have been actually working with Townsend.) Of Townsend's character, Benjamin Tallmadge wrote: "This much I can assure you — he is a Gentleman of business, of Education and honor." General Washington wrote, in reference to Townsend and his associate Abraham Woodhull (also known as Culper): "Of the Culpers' fidelity and ability I entertain the highest opinion."

Very real, too, were Austin Roe, the greatest courier who traveled the deadly Secret Road between Manhattan and Setauket; Caleb Brewster, the oddly employed artilleryman and his whaleboat fleet;

and, of course, the presiding genius — Benjamin Tallmadge, Major of Continental Dragoons.

The codes, aliases and methods used in this book are drawn from Mr. Pennypacker. Actually, Robert Townsend was known as "Samuel Culper, Junior" or simply "Culper Junior," while Abraham Woodhull was addressed as "Culper Senior." For the sake of clarity I have omitted Woodhull's alias, since the "Senior" suggests Robert Townsend's father, Samuel Townsend of Raynham Hall. The secret ink which figures in this story seems to have been perfected in London by James Jay and smuggled to his brother, John Jay, and thence to Washington and Tallmadge.

Many of the incidents in this book actually happened. Others are based on what *could* have happened within the known framework of fact. The delivery of the John Anderson letter to Major André at Raynham Hall is based on a legend in the Townsend family in which Sarah Townsend played the chief role, rather than the fictitious Polly Morgan. The attack on the French gold is entirely imaginary, but possible.

So, mingling fact and fiction, this is a story of the Secret Road and of the people who operated it, men and women who worked in quiet devotion, always in deadly peril and usually cloaked in an anonymity which has endured almost to our own day.

BRUCE LANCASTER

Beverly, Massachusetts

CONTENTS

Foreword   vii

    I Samuel Culper, Esq.   3

   II The Road to the Sound   18

  III United States Dragoon   34

   IV The Beacons   56

    V Laurel Dane   80

   VI In Enemy Country   104

  VII Pursuit   133

 VIII John Anderson   162

   IX The Desperate Gamble   180

    X The Midnight Visitor   215

   XI French Gold   232

  XII Rescue   248

THE SECRET ROAD

I

Samuel Culper, Esq.

In the hush of a July afternoon in 1780, His Majesty's Transport *Avon* dropped anchor just off the lower end of Manhattan Island. A detail of Royal Marines filed out onto the deck and quickly posted themselves by the afterhatch. A marine captain with a worn, thoughtful face turned from the rail where he had been studying the low sprawl of the city of New York, and acknowledged the salute of the sergeant in charge. "Will I bring the prisoners aloft now, sir?" the latter asked.

The captain nodded wearily. Then he seemed to change his mind. "No," he said. "Bring the special prisoner first. I want to talk to him alone."

The sergeant stared, then beckoned to two privates who thereupon vanished down the companionway. In a few moments they returned. The prisoner was tall with a spare, rangy build and his brown hair was cut unfashionably short. He halted before the captain and spoke in a level tone, as if he were addressing an equal rather than a captor. "Lieutenant Grant Ledyard reporting, sir." His gray eyes surveyed the deck. He seemed quite at ease despite his tattered brown cavalry jacket and broken shoes.

"Ledyard," the captain said gravely, "I can't send you off with the other prisoners. You've been ordered to the prison hulks in the harbor."

"You consider that a fair ruling, Captain?"

"Well — h'm — really, I can't comment on that," said the captain hastily. "You had no business striking the officer of the guard that night."

"You witnessed the provocation, Captain. He kicked that South Carolina boy who was down with scurvy. He called him a stinking, rebel bastard. I gave him ample chance to defend himself." Grant spoke tersely, without emotion.

The marine inclined his head. "So I testified at the hearing. But the ruling stands. A boat's waiting for you overside. Damn it, Ledyard, I don't like this any better than you do. Those hulks — well, it can't be helped. In any event, I don't think you'll be there long."

"No?" asked Grant. "Why do you say that?"

"Why, the war will soon be over for us both! Look at what's happened! You started fighting in '75. Here it is '80 and you're getting shakier all the time. Nothing's gone right for you since Burgoyne blundered into your trap in '77. Last summer, even with the help of the French army and fleet at Savannah, we beat you with a smaller force. This year we took Charleston and General Lincoln's whole army, yourself included. We control everything south of Virginia. Washington's army up on the Hudson is without money, food or equipment. His men are deserting. He simply couldn't move a force against us. And your people are indifferent. They are defeated. Capitulation must come soon, and with it a general release of prisoners. That's why I don't think your stay in the prison hulk will be a long one."

Grant smiled. "We've been losing this war since '75. But you haven't been winning it."

"But we shall. Good-by, Ledyard, and good luck."

Two marines closed in on either side of Grant as he stepped to a gap in the bulwarks where the rope ladder dangled. For an instant he stood poised, his eyes sweeping the scenes before him. There was the Battery with its bristle of British guns at the foot of Manhattan. He saw the ruined spire of Trinity Church and, beyond it, the cupola of the New York Hospital. East, toward the river, broken rooflines showed, empty spaces that had been chewed out of the skyline by the great fires that had struck the city during the war. The East River and the Bay below it dazzled in the brilliance of the late-afternoon sun, and masts of many craft thrust awkwardly toward the sky. Somewhere in the heart of the blinding shimmer lay the hulk to which his British captors were sending him, one of the rotten, deadly, floating prisons from which, he knew, few men emerged alive.

"Now, sir, if you please," said the marine sergeant at his elbow.

Grant swung down the ladder. When he stepped on the rocking planks of the longboat, he looked south toward Staten Island. The glare, less intense, was being slowly replaced by an unhealthy coppery-yellow. A brisk wind whipped up, and whitecaps showed on the water. "Dirty weather brewing," a sailor muttered. The marines followed Grant into the boat and the oars cut clean into the water as they struck out for the Long Island shore.

Masses of inky clouds rolled up and all at once the whole harbor was shrouded in menacing gloom. As the boat swayed and tossed in the rising wind, rain dashed down in sheets. Grant could barely make out the shouts and curses of the sailors. Then an oar snapped and the boat swung broadside to the storm. A mass of water roared over the thwarts, drenching Grant. He struck at the nearest sailor shouting, "Back to the *Avon!* We can't live in this sea!" The waves pounded against the boat and again broke over the stern. One marine and the helmsman were washed overboard. Now the boat stood nearly upright, bow to stern, pitched, dove. Grant clutched at the nearest thwart, but a sudden swirl of water plunged him into the East River. Out of a welter of foam and spray an arm caught his, tugged, was gone.

Water filled his mouth and his eyes, whirled him right and then left, caught at his legs and swung them upward. Then his face was above water, the rain tearing against it. No one else was near him. His arms and legs flailed on and on, desperately. Once his down-thrust legs jarred against bottom and he rallied himself for a last heave to shore, but the sweep of the river drew him back again, then hurled him out on solid ground. He fell face downward,

5

crawled, coughing and gasping, until blackness came over him.

When his senses returned, the gale was still howling and the rain slashing down. He looked dizzily about. He was on a sloping wooden ramp that led out from the New York water front. Right and left were stone piers, and against these, waves were breaking with a frantic roar. Here and there, floating docks, partially ripped away, swayed wildly. There was no sign of his guards.

Grant wiped his streaming face and took stock of his position. From his early service in New York, before it fell to the Crown forces, he recognized the place as Coenties Slip. The water front was deserted. He got unsteadily to his feet and bending to the force of the gale, moved forward cautiously, a plan maturing in his mind.

The storm had driven every living soul indoors. Perhaps he could make his way up the water front past the city limits of New York and then strike for the open country. Under cover of night an agile man might work past the British outposts into Westchester County and thence to the American lines. It was just possible.

"It's better than the hulks," he muttered. "I'll get to our lines and then ― well, maybe that marine captain was right about the war's being nearly over."

On unsteady legs he made his way along the water front. First he must find a cloak to cover his cavalry jacket. Drenched as the garment was, its colors would attract any military eye and lead to disastrous questions. But how could he come by a cloak? Even if he had had money, he would not dare enter any of the water front shops. Stray soldiers of the Crown, sheltering from the storm, would certainly question him.

Then he noticed the shacks which hung over the water, places where boatmen stored oars, tackle and goods waiting shipment across to Long Island. In one of them he might find what he needed. Slowly he fought his way toward the nearest shack. As he approached it, a heavy wave cut sidewise along the shore and pulled the flimsy structure into the river. The next hut, set farther back

6

from the edge, showed a dull glow of orange light and he sheered away from it.

More lights gleamed along the inland side, a tavern, a ship chandler's, a saddler's. Then down a side street he saw a squad of British soldiers struggling to lash a tarpaulin over a stack of crates, and the sight of the scarlet uniforms sent him hurrying on, heart pounding.

Ahead on his right, a shed door swung slowly open, revealing a pitch-dark interior. He stopped, crouching, waiting to see who might emerge. The door shook, slammed shut, opened again. "Empty!" he whispered and sprinted toward it. Inside the air was dry and smelled of leather, spices, salt. His groping hands found bales, packing cases, chests. Then his fingers wound about a cloak hanging from a peg in the wall. He threw its worn folds about him and reached for a battered hat, his hands shaking.

As he turned toward the door, he gasped. There stood a slim man, rain sluicing off a cocked hat and long cloak. As the wind turned the cloak back, Grant saw underneath a red coat, red waistcoat and white breeches. "I think it would be a good idea for you to come along with me," the stranger said pleasantly, in a conversational tone.

Grant tried to match the other's tone. "There could be two opinions about that," he said.

"Oh, I think not," observed the man urbanely, and Grant heard the dry snick of a pistol-hammer being drawn back.

The stranger went on. "I was in that tavern back there," he said, "not far from Coenties Slip. I saw you through the window. It seemed odd to me that you kept on through the storm. Then I noted your uniform. Soaked though it is, its cut suggested several interesting possibilities to me. Hence, I followed you." He stepped clear of the door. "Now come with me, please."

Grant hesitated, then gathered his cloak and left the shed. The other closed in behind him and Grant felt the hard muzzle of a pistol against his spine. The voice went on, "Take that alley ahead of us."

The wind had gone down a little but the rain fell in sullen streams. Grant entered the alley, eyes and mind alert. He thought of dropping suddenly to his knees, turning as he fell. Or there might be a doorway into which he could duck and then spring out. He had not had a good look at his captor and knew only that he was young and about average height and weight. He had no doubt that if it came to plain grappling, he could handle the man without much trouble but the prodding of the pistol warned him to wait.

They splashed on. A turn to the right into a wider alley, to the left through a dripping stable yard where hens clucked forlornly, right again along a paved street. Somewhere behind them, boots squelched, army boots. Then his captor said, "Into that archway, on your left. Face inward. Quiet, now."

Fear tugged at Grant as the boots came closer. He was sure the stranger would hail the patrol and turn him over. But the soldiers passed on.

The stranger explained, "A detail of the Twelfth. They might have tried to nobble you up and claim credit for you at headquarters, which would be rather unfair since it was I who braved the storm to trail you. Now — that white brick house on your right, the one with the outer steps leading to the second floor. Go right up and unlock the door." He thrust a heavy key into Grant's palm. "I'll be close behind you."

Grant pushed open the door and paused on the threshold in surprise. The room was large. A lamp on a mahogany table threw out a pale glow. There were deep rugs on the floor, broad-seated chairs, a painting or two on the walls. Books were everywhere, in cases, on the table, stacked in chairs, on the floor. The stranger said patiently, "Do you mind going in? I'd rather like to get out of the rain myself."

"May I ask if this is a sample guardroom?" Grant asked dryly as he entered.

8

The other laughed. "It's the sort of dungeon that I'd design, if I were to be the prisoner. These are my own quarters. First, you'd better get dry. Go through that door beyond the fireplace. I'll find you a change of clothes. Don't look for a possible exit from that room because there is none."

"Your solicitude overwhelms me," said Grant. He bowed ironically and passed into the closetlike room with its single tiny window.

In a moment the man tossed him clothes and a towel. Grant sat down on the carved wooden chest, heedless of the water oozing from his boots. He was worried and bewildered. This fellow was a cool hand, but beyond that, what was he? Grant had caught a glimpse of what seemed to be a uniform under his cloak, but nothing to identify a regiment or a branch of the service. Was the man actually a British soldier? The way he had spoken of the patrol made it seem he was with the army, but not of it. Perhaps a volunteer hoping for a commission? Gentleman-adventurer? His unconventional handling of a prisoner suggested that he was not a member of any rigid organization. "In any event," Grant told himself, "this isn't over yet. All I've got to do is keep my wits about me."

He rubbed himself vigorously with the towel, then reached for the clothes. The underwear was good linen and the ruffled shirt fitted him well enough. For trousers he had been given long, brown coveralls of the type issued to the Highland regiments when the North American mosquitoes forced them to abandon their kilts.

When he was dressed, Grant stepped into the main room. His captor had discarded the red uniform coat and waistcoat and sat behind a flat desk in a finely-woven linen shirt. Pistol before him, he looked up with an amiable smile and politely indicated a chair by the desk. "Sit down, Mr. — ah — " began the stranger.

He seemed about twenty-five. Neatly dressed black hair framed a frank, open face. He looked like a man who found the world a pleasant place, full of agreeable people. His benevolent look was almost overtrustful. Grant remembered that the hand that held the pistol back in the shed had been steady.

"Ledyard — Grant Ledyard of Bland's dragoons," Grant answered calmly.

"Exactly. Your uniform told your regiment, Mr. Ledyard. My name is Robert Townsend. Now as to your case — "

"Mr. Robert Townsend of — ?" Grant left the question unfinished.

Townsend smiled pleasantly. "Of the city of New York. No, please don't eye that pistol. It's not loaded, but the one in this open drawer is. Now tell me. Mr. Ledyard, how does it happen that an officer of Bland's finds himself running through a tropical gale along the New York water front?"

Grant considered plausible fiction against truth and decided on the truth. "I was taken when General Lincoln surrendered at Charleston."

Townsend's eyes narrowed. "I was not aware that Bland's people were there."

Grant looked up, surprised that Townsend should be so well posted. "They weren't," he explained. "I was on command — detached to serve with Lincoln's staff. After the surrender, a lot of us were shipped up here. This noon, I was transferred to a longboat, headed for the prison hulks. On the voyage up here, I'd taken exception to a swine in charge of prisoners."

The other cocked his head indulgently. "Laudable, perhaps, but impulsive. Go on."

Grant told of the storm and his luck in being swept ashore. "I thought I had a fighting chance of working north to our army," he concluded.

"Interesting, most interesting, Mr. Ledyard." Townsend placed his fingertips together and regarded them quizzically. "As your captor, I think I have something to say about your eventual disposition. I've never approved of the hulks. I may be able to find a spot for you on Long Island. That would be my preference, if I'm able to — " He looked up with an air of pleased expectancy as voices and steps sounded on the outside stairs. "I have callers, Mr. Ledyard. Would you mind stepping into your dressing room for a few moments? I suggest you close the door for your own comfort."

Grant sat in the little room, his head in his hands. He had begun the interview with confidence, but he had learned nothing of Townsend's motives or plans.

In the other room Grant heard Townsend exclaiming. "Payson! Drummond! A great pleasure. Has it really stopped raining? Pull up some chairs. How are things with the Twenty-fourth?"

Messrs. Payson and Drummond, (junior officers of the Twenty-fourth, Grant guessed) were making a great to-do over their host. "Look, Townie, my dear old fellow. Brought this bottle of brandy right from Sir Henry's table . . . hoped we'd find you . . . the major was asking about you, most particular. . . ."

Grant listened uneasily to the blur of conversation, but could find no clue that threw light on Robert Townsend. What the devil was he up to? The hum of voices and the clink of glasses buzzed exasperatingly. Grant examined the little window carefully, then turned away, disappointed. Escape, if it were to be contrived, would have to be won through Townsend's strange obstinacy in handling the case himself.

In the other room, one of the guests was speaking persuasively, almost wheedling. " . . . it's a fine line of works we've thrown up. Runs east from Fort Knyphausen — you know, what the rebels used to call Fort Washington. It's a picture! The minute the last spade of earth was turned, I said to old Drummond, here, I said, 'Townie ought to see this.' "

"Yes, that's just what Jimmy said to me. Be a good chap and come out with us, see it for yourself. We'll turn out a guard for you, make a regular field day of it."

"H'm. I don't know." Townsend sounded dubious. "It's pretty far out to Harlem Plains."

"Do you good! We'll find you a carriage. Jove, I can see right now the sort of article you'd write for the *Gazette*. A Gibraltar on Manhattan, manned by the good old Twenty-fourth."

Doubt was heavier in Townsend's voice. "But Rivington was saying just the other day that he'd been using too much military stuff."

"Here, here, Jim. Fill up Townie's glass. A day out in the country, mess with us — " the speaker's voice dropped a little — besides, dash it all — well, you know that what you write for Rivington is read by Sir Henry and it's read in London. I know for a fact that Curzon got his step because of your story about his bringing in those horses from Westchester. Wayland was taken onto staff after you wrote about his finding champagne for the Riedesels' reception." His tones grew flatter. "Townie — just a line about the works and perhaps about the way old Drummond edged the ornamental walk to the ajax by sinking up-ended bottles along it. Dash it all, I've been lieutenant for eleven years and Drummond for eight!"

"So Townsend's a scribbler!" thought Grant. "But why the uniform?" He wondered if the man was merely trying to ease the boredom of occupied New York by writing for the *Gazette*.

Grant heard Townsend say, "I'll do what I can," and one of the guests exclaim, "That's handsome of you, Townie, dashed handsome." The outer door closed and the two men thumped down the stairs.

"You may come in now," Townsend called to Grant.

"I couldn't help overhearing, you know," Grant said as he seated himself.

Townsend made a deprecatory gesture. "They vastly overrate my small influence. Now about yourself, Mr. Ledyard?"

Grant felt a tightening in his chest. "Is it too much to hope that your influence may extend to me? I know that devil Cunningham's still in charge of prisoners. If I'm to be one, I don't want to be under him."

"I can understand that," observed Townsend. "I'll do what I can to send you to Long Island." He smiled.

"You'll send me under guard from your own regiment?"

"My regiment, Mr. Ledyard? I have none."

"But your uniform —"

"Oh, that." Townsend gave a negligent wave of the hand. "Sir Henry has drafted some of our citizens to serve as guards at his quarters now and then. It's held to be a distinction, even if we do pay for our own uniforms. I'm not a soldier. I haven't the temperament. I'd even call myself timid. In me, you behold a loyal New York merchant, who enjoys some slight standing with the military, and who amuses himself by writing for James Rivington's *Gazette.*"

Grant's mouth twisted in a wry smile. "Are you trying to increase your influence by turning me in?"

Townsend made a clucking noise. "A harsh way of putting it — Ah! More steps outside. No, you stay."

A slight, sharp-faced man slipped into the room and Townsend beamed a welcome. "Prompt as always, Austin. This is Mr. Grant Ledyard, a rebel lieutenant, late of Bland's dragoons. Mr. Ledyard, this is Austin Roe, a friend who looks after my Long Island customers."

Roe bowed, and gave Grant a look that carried an odd hint of approval. Then he turned to Townsend. "What's to go tomorrow, Rob?"

"I'm afraid it will be tonight."

Roe shook his head. "Better wait. The army's sealed up the island tight. No one leaves. No one comes in."

Townsend nodded. "Just the same, I'd like it to be tonight, Austin. There are some letters. This one in particular —" he held it up — "is for Colonel Floyd, explaining why I can't fill his order just now for the goods to replace those he lost when the rebels

13

burned him out." He added, as though to himself, "Most important — that letter for Floyd."

Without a change of expression, Roe said, "I'll go."

"Thank you, Austin. I knew you would. Now those parcels in the corner," Townsend went on, "ribbons, laces, fiddle-faddles to go in your bags. This letter paper is for Mr. John Bolton, care of Abraham Woodhull at Setauket. Mr. Ledyard, I'm going to count off a few of these sheets aloud, and I'd be obliged if you'd keep in mind the number at which I stop. One, two, three, four — Jove this is good paper. Wonder where Rivington gets it. Five, six — "

Grant watched, the frown deepening on his forehead. The setting, the people, their words and actions were baffling. Townsend stopped counting at twenty-five, humming lightly to himself. The second pack was treated in the same way, Townsend reaching a tally of thirty-three. "Twenty-five and thirty-three," he remarked. "You'll both remember?"

"Both?" cried Grant.

"Yes. Austin Roe is your escort to Long Island."

Grant flushed. "Look here, Townsend, why ask me to mix in your private business? And why are you sending me to Long Island with just one man for a guard? There's no sense in this. I'll do everything I can to escape and get back to the American army. You know it as well as I do."

Roe and Townsend exchanged glances. The latter said, "Since I'm taking steps to see that you do not come under the care of the provost, Cunningham, I feel justified in asking this favor of you. I'd like you to see to the delivery of this writing paper to the men who ordered it."

"What the devil is all this?" snapped Grant. "If your man at Setauket really wants that paper, you'd better see to it yourself."

Townsend interposed blandly. "Let me describe the recipient, Mr. Ledyard. John Bolton, care of Abraham Woodhull. Mr. Bolton, whom you will not find at Setauket, is a youngish man. Tall —

about as tall as you. He's what my friends in the Royal Marines would call long-sparred. Most people call him handsome. He's a graduate of Yale College and a man of parts. You'll find him most humane."

"You're trying to tell me that he's in charge of the prison where you're sending me?" asked Grant.

Roe chuckled. "He's in charge of a good many things."

"You say he's from Yale? A Tory?"

"Not precisely," said Townsend. "As I remarked, you will not find him at Setauket, nor will he answer to the name of John Bolton. You will address him as Major Benjamin Tallmadge, when you meet him in — " he paused, "in Fairfield, Connecticut."

For a moment Grant could only stare at Robert Townsend in shock and disbelief. Benjamin Tallmadge! Though junior to Tallmadge, Grant had developed a profound admiration and liking for him, knew that he was reckoned one of the very best of the American cavalry leaders, and a devout patriot. "I knew there was something rotten here," Grant cried hoarsely, jumping to his feet. "You'll never make me believe that Ben Tallmadge has turned traitor!"

Townsend shook his head gravely. "Not a traitor, Mr. Ledyard."

Grant looked incredulously at Townsend. At length he said in a shaky voice, "This is true? You're playing no tricks on me?"

"No tricks, Mr. Ledyard."

"Then why in God's name didn't you tell me you were on our side?"

"My dear Mr. Ledyard," protested Townsend gently, "first I had to find out exactly who and what you were. I am in no position to allow myself the luxury of an error. I talked with you, I watched you. I liked, among other things, the straight way you accounted for yourself. Above all, your catching at the slimmest chances of getting back to your own army. Then I made up my mind. I will help you rejoin the army, as I have been able to help one or two others who have found themselves in your approximate situation. Really, it's all very simple."

Grant struggled for composure as he sank back in his chair, bewilderment giving way to admiration for the pleasant, smiling man opposite him. He managed to say, "You mean that you live here all the time, on good terms with the British Army?"

Townsend raised a protesting hand. "But why should you be surprised? I am no soldier. As I remarked, I am essentially a timid man. I often regret that my constitution forces me to live at ease in a comfortable city. I simply do what I can."

Grant looked about the mellow, book-filled room, which was in startling contrast with Robert Townsend's dangerous calling. Townsend went about New York, day after day, in deadly peril every second. His agent, Austin Roe. must court equal danger. His realization of their great courage left him feeling oddly humble.

"Now about your journey," Townsend went on. "When you meet Major Tallmadge you'll give him these packs of paper, repeating to him the numbers that I asked you to remember. You must mention, too, the name of Samuel Culper. That's all you'll need to tell him, just Samuel Culper. That's how I'm known on your side. You and Austin better start now. I've written your name on this pass along with Austin's, but I don't think you'll have to show it if you bring out the letter to Colonel Floyd first. Here's a dry cloak for you and a carter's hat."

Grant clapped on the broad hat, slung the cape over his arm. He tried to put some of his emotions into words as he shook hands with Townsend, but could only stammer out lamely, "This work of yours — never heard of anything like it — don't see how I can thank you enough for myself. For the rest of it — "

"Nonsense," said Townsend. "Good luck, Mr. Ledyard. This has been a most propitious day for me. In you the army has regained a seasoned cavalry officer, and I have found a friend. Here are your saddlebags, with the letter paper. Don't worry about your journey. In case of doubt, remember that success often lies in bold-ness. Ready, Austin?"

Saddlebags over his arm, Grant clattered down the steps after Austin Roe. Halfway down, he turned, looked back. Robert Town-send stood in the doorway watching them. His face wore a look of deep concern. Then as he met Grant's eyes, the easy smile returned. He raised a hand in farewell and closed the door.

II

The Road to the Sound

At the bottom step Grant drew back uncertainly. Roe was talking with two men in British uniform. They barely glanced at Grant, but even so, he felt a growing panic. When the soldiers turned and started up the steps, Roe looked sympathetically at Grant. "It's all right. They're just going up to tell Rob about changes in the embarkation plans." He hitched at his saddlebags. "Come on," he said, starting off down the street.

Grant fell in beside Roe, and tried to rally himself. He forced his gait to an easy stride and swung the saddlebags nonchalantly. He must be calm, must mingle naturally with others so that he could escape notice. He must remember that he was supposed to have followed this same route many times in the past, carrying on a not too exacting trade. He knew that any behavior which attracted attention would be highly dangerous. His confidence returned slowly as he began to whistle "A Health to King Charles."

As they walked along the narrow street Grant noticed that the trim houses alternated with roofless shells, relics of the great fire of '76. A knot of boys, whooping and screeching, pelted past them and plunged into one of the charred doorways. Grant looked west toward Broadway with its double line of trees. He saw coaches rolling ponderously along, pattened girls jumping over flooded gutters and liveried servants carrying baskets.

At Dock Street Roe turned left. Grant followed close behind, edging into the throng that choked the narrow sidewalk. Over his head swung the signs of ironmongers, chandlers, sugar merchants, liquor dealers, clothiers — Brinckerhoff, Cuyler & Van Dam, Clarkson & Sebring, Duyckinck the sailmaker. The air was laden with the smell of coffee and tar and hides and cobbler's wax, of spices and rum. Over the heads of the crowd, he could see the East River, still tossing heavily. Most of the people, he noticed, were slowing down, fanning right and left as they neared a broad wharf. Then his heart jumped in alarm. A squad of infantry guarded the wharf and a tall lieutenant was shouting at the crowd, "Ferry's closed! No passage till further notice."

Grant watched the people sullenly drift away, grumbling. But Roe pressed right on, elbowing and slipping through the press of men and women, until he faced the angry lieutenant, who shouted at him. "Blast it, man! Don't you understand English. Ferry's closed till — oh, it's you, is it, Roe? Sorry. Orders are out."

Roe said something quietly to the lieutenant. The man looked uncertain, then said, "Let me see it."

Roe pulled out the letter to Colonel Floyd and the pass for them both. Grant found himself trembling. If his true identity were to be discovered now, his case would be absolutely hopeless. He was a soldier in enemy territory and he was in civilian clothes. Under military law he was therefore a spy. He heard the lieutenant say hesitantly, "Letter from Rob Townsend for Floyd. I don't know — I guess it's right enough. But we'll have to search you, you know."

Roe jerked his head at Grant who came forward, mouth dry and knees stiff. A sergeant reached for the saddlebags, went through them and handed them back without comment. Then he ran his hands up and down Grant's body. "Nothing here, sir!" The guards stepped aside and Grant followed Roe onto the bargelike ferry.

The boat was empty save for themselves and the crew. Grant watched the receding shores where a sinking sun lit up the roofs and ruins of Manhattan. Somewhere under those roofs, Townsend, who had called himself timid, was chatting amiably with officers of the King whose words would be sent across this same East

19

River, the length of Long Island, and over the Sound where they would be read by a Major Benjamin Tallmadge, sometimes addressed as Mr. John Bolton.

The passage was not so rough as the first glimpse of the river had promised, but signs of the storm were all around them. Swamped skiffs rocked in the current. Grant saw drifting spars, the pinkish side of a drowned pig, a child's hat, sodden and tragic. He shivered a little. He felt empty and discouraged. What could the future hold for him and his country? What if he did get through and rejoin the army, an army that seemed always on the verge of melting away? Would there be only more years of inconclusive and wasted campaigns, of poor equipment and starvation rations?

The barge was now swinging in by a stubby pier to the north of the main wharves of Brooklyn. At the throat of the pier a detail of men stood guard. As soon as the barge was moored Roe sprang out nimbly and Grant followed, clumsily tripping over his own load. "Remember," he told himself, "safety lies in boldness."

He saw the detail stiffen and two sergeants cross their halberds over the barrier gate. A wan, consumptive ensign appeared and stared at the civilians with their saddlebags. Grant looked quickly over the side of the pier, weighing his chances of plunging into the river and swimming away.

The ensign spoke to Roe. "What the devil! No one's supposed to be crossing today! What are you trying to do?"

Roe slowly drew out his papers. "My pass. Signed by the officer in charge at Coenties."

The ensign scowled at the sheet. "Signed, is it? A blind beggar could have made that scrawl. You better be careful, Roe. A lot of people have been wondering about you lately, asking questions about you."

"Girls, probably," Roe answered lightly.

"Girls be damned. Here! What's that other paper you've got?"

He snatched it from Roe's hand. Then his expression changed. "A letter for Colonel Floyd. Why didn't you tell me?"

"Didn't ask me."

At a signal from the ensign, the men stood back from the barrier gate. Grant pulled at his saddlebags and lounged through, forcing himself to stop on the other side to adjust a shoebuckle. When he raised his head he saw a major coming down the path that led to the main wharves. The major strode briskly, swinging a silver-topped stick. Then he looked their way and gave the stick a sudden flourish and stopped. "Roe!" he cried. His pop-eyes surveyed them amiably enough but Grant thought he could see temper in that tight mouth.

"How's my good friend Townsend? Off up the island, are you? Where are your beasts?" the major asked.

"At Onderdonk's Inn yonder," answered Roe, ignoring the first questions.

"Going the Jamaica route?" asked the major, polishing the head of his stick on his red sleeve.

Roe shook his head. "Flushing. Quicker. Got a letter for Colonel Floyd."

The major looked thoughtful. "Flushing? You armed? These are rackety times. Roads aren't safe."

"There'll be pistols in our holsters at Onderdonk's," Roe assured him.

"Come into the guardhouse for a minute," the major said. "Maybe you can help me."

Roe nodded and followed the major into a rough hut nearby. Grant sat on a stump by the path to wait. The ensign and his fusiliers paid no attention to him and for the moment he felt safe. He noticed fresh-turned earth beyond the hut, and idly strolled over to investigate. He found himself looking down into an expertly constructed gun emplacement where a pair of twelve-pounders stood, well sited to cover the approaches to the pier. Grant dropped into the pit and squinted along the barrels.

Suddenly something rapped on his shoulder. He turned to find the major, his face purple, prodding him with his stick. Behind him stood Roe, obviously alarmed. "By God, damned insolence. What the devil do you mean?" the major spluttered. "Setting yourself up as Inspector General of Ordnance."

Grant heard himself saying, "Oh, I thought you knew. I'm a spy."

Unexpectedly the major burst into a roar of laughter. "A spy!" he shouted. "Jove, that's good! My apologies! I never interfere with an honest man at his trade. Now you'd better run along, you two." He raised his stick in farewell and stumped off, still chuckling.

As Roe and Grant set off up a path that branched north, Roe said approvingly, "That was a smart answer you gave the major. Now let's hurry. The major tells me we'll find company at Onderdonk's."

The trail now dipped into a grassy hollow, scarred with earthworks of '76. Roe stopped to hand Grant the letter to Floyd.

Grant took it with surprise. "What should I do with it?" he asked.

"Give it to John Bolton. Maybe he'll forward it. I doubt it." He raised a warning hand as Grant started to speak.

When they topped the crest, Grant saw a sandy road twisting away to the northeast and in the distance a long, white, low-roofed tavern with stables beyond. A heavy chaise stood in front. Grant, looked questioningly at Roe.

"Must belong to the company I mentioned. Major wants us to see two ladies safe to Setauket." He lowered his voice. "The army hates to admit it, but the roads aren't safe. Been everything from arson to murder."

Grant frowned. "We could be delayed by these ladies."

"Could be. But it'll pay. The major's pleased, and I've found its kind of healthy to have men in red uniforms smiling when they see me."

Their long shadows bobbed and danced ahead of them in the last rays of the sun as they approached the inn. "You'd best wait outside," said Roe. "I'll go in and see about the ladies and about our horses." Without another glance, he glided into the inn.

Grant leaned against the wall and sniffed enviously at the appetizing smells that oozed out into the summer evening. There was coffee and fresh bread and the fine, meaty aroma that told of roasts. Then he remembered that he had eaten nothing since morning, when he had had some hard salt beef and a broth of wormy peas on the Avon. Was it only that morning? So much had happened in so few hours! The storm, his escape from drowning, his desperate run up the water front, Robert Townsend, the ferry —

He felt a touch at his elbow. A small boy in a leather apron held out a plate and a mug and scurried away as Grant took them, eagerly surveying rare roast beef, potatoes, bread. The mug gave out a comforting reek of rum and water. The window at his left was open, and he rested plate and mug on the broad sill. His world, for the moment, shrank to that sill and what was on it. The beef was rich and tender, the potatoes swam in good butter and the bread was still warm from the oven.

A large, yellow cat sprang into the window, curled its tail about its feet and regarded Grant solemnly through golden eyes. Grant raised his mug. "Your health, sir," he said. Then he set the mug down and peered through the window, attracted by a stir within.

The room into which he looked was empty, but beyond it was a larger one, and a girl was sitting at a table. A mass of golden hair framed a small face with a broad forehead and delicate eyebrows. Chin resting in her hand, she was looking straight ahead of her, her mouth firmly set as though she were deep in thought — serious, perhaps troubling thought. "Hello!" he said to himself. "I never expected anything like *this* in a Long Island tavern. "What's she doing here? Reminds me a little of — " In his memory he saw another girl alighting from a carriage outside the Harvard Yard — still another waving to him from the balcony of a house near Morristown as he rode out with his dragoons — a third along the Battery in Charleston. But they were all far away in both space

23

and time. He eyed her more closely, wondering at her absorption. "What's she got on her mind? She looks as if she were planning a campaign. How would it be if — maybe I could attract her attention." Then the voice of an older woman sounded from some other room. "Laurel! Are you ready?" The girl rose lightly and her whole expression changed. Grant saw that she was strikingly pretty and her full lips turned up in a quick smile. "Coming, Aunt Ann!" she called, and there was no trace of worry in her tone or expression. "Campaign be blasted," thought Grant, leaning slightly to catch a last glimpse of her. "She was probably trying to decide which mantua to wear!"

Grant finished his hasty meal as Roe appeared in the doorway, pointing to a stableboy, who was leading out a pair of saddled horses. Roe pointed to the nearer, a fine-limbed gray. "That's yours. Better mount up."

As Grant tested the girth he remarked, "Did you happen to see that very pretty girl in the — "

"Aren't any pretty girls in this work," said Roe shortly. "Noticing such things can give a man a sore throat." He made an expressive gesture. "From having hemp around it."

"I suppose so," said Grant. "How about the major's ladies, have you seen them?"

"They're ready. Coming now."

As Roe spoke, a jockeylike Negro drove a chaise out of the stable yard. The inn door opened; a tall, elderly woman in sober gray came out and climbed into the vehicle.

Then Grant heard the patter of heels inside the inn, saw a figure emerge into the gathering gloom. In a flurry of dark cloak which showed a red-gold lining, the girl whom he had seen earlier ran out, a red-lined bonnet swinging from her hand.

The girl was one of the major's ladies! He looked down at her from his saddle. She was even prettier than in profile, and her wide-set eyes were deep brown. The girl smiled up at him as she got into the chaise. She looked about twenty, and the warmth of her expression set his heart beating unexpectedly. He was keenly aware of his nondescript clothes, his floppy carter's hat and the rough stubble about chin and cheeks, but remembered that his clothes matched his role, that it was his armor for this voyage. He managed to bob his head awkwardly, to touch the brim of his hat with a gruff, "Servant, miss."

The chaise rolled away along the brownish track that led to Flushing and the north shore of Long Island. Grant paced his gray beside Roe's bay in the rear of the carriage. "How do you want to manage this thing?" he asked.

"Alternate front and rear. I'll ride ahead as long as the light lasts. Then you come up for a spell," said Roe tersely.

"Any special instructions?"

"Two. Remember you're scouting in enemy country. And crook that back of yours. You're just a countryman on a horse." Roe clucked to his horse and trotted out some twenty yards in front of the chaise.

Grant slumped in the saddle as best as he could and turned his eyes away from the chaise. He told himself the girl was pretty, but unimportant. He wondered why she was under the major's protection.

He tried to study the country, to think how this open terrain would look to him if he were scouting it with his dragoons. The visibility, so long as the least light lasted, was so wide that he would not have needed to send out flankers right and left.

All at once he realized that he was not only thinking like a dragoon, but riding like one. He slumped again. The road was growing softer, muffling the crunch of the wheels and the slap of hoofs. He could hear the elder woman speaking, though the words were lost in the evening air. Then the girl spoke. Her voice was low and musical. Again he wondered who she was.

The wheels struck harder ground, blanketing the voices. Light was fading fast and soon Roe would call him to take the lead. He unbuckled the holster that hung on either side of the pommel and knew sudden assurance as he drew the pistols out. They were British made, rifled and double-barreled, and each holster held a little mallet for driving home a fresh charge. Roe trotted back to him. "Make it fifty yards ahead," ordered Roe.

"All quiet?"

"Always is — till the last minute."

Grant gave a wry laugh. "And what might happen in that last minute? No one's seen fit to tell me much."

"I told you before. Marauders or robbers. Might be deserters from both sides or local folk who don't mind picking up a sixpence or a bale of goods." As Grant rode off, Roe called, "Fifty yards, mind."

The chaise showed only a white blur of faces as Grant trotted past. The darkness grew thicker and the stars hung high and faint. There was just enough light to mark the way.

At the top of a low rise, Grant suddenly straightened up. Ahead he saw a dancing beam of light that grew brighter and brighter. A touch of his knees and the gray slowed obediently. Then he realized that danger would come only from the darkness, and not from the light ahead. At last he could make out the legs of horses and the glint of metal and a voice called hoarsely, "Who's there? Pull up, I say."

A high-held lantern shone in Grant's eyes and he saw mounted men in red milling about him. A hard-faced officer looked suspiciously at him from under a brass helmet. "Account for yourself," he said sharply.

Grant tried to make his voice sullen, but steady. "Taking a letter to Colonel Floyd from Mr. Robert Townsend."

"Show me the letter and your pass," said the officer.

Grant handed over the letter, taking care that the lantern light fell on the inscription. The officer grunted, "For Floyd right enough, but anyone can write a letter to Floyd. Let's see what this is." He shook out the unsealed sheets and stared at them, his pursed-out underlip shiny in the light. The half-circle of troopers

26

stirred and shifted while he read, and Grant became restless under the scrutiny of at least a dozen pairs of eyes.

The officer's hard face eased. He pushed the letter into Grant's hand, and turned to speak to a subaltern behind him. "No question about this. I know Floyd had to order a lot of goods from Townsend after those damned rebels burned him out. Townsend just says there'll be some delay, but he'll do the best he can." He turned to Grant. "Man named Roe usually rides for Townsend. Where's he?"

"Back on the road, sir. Looking after a chaiseload of women for some major of the Brooklyn garrison. Shall I call him?"

"No need." He gathered his horse. "I know Townsend and Roe well enough. Take 'em off, sergeant. Right by trooper! March!" The patrol filed away down a path that led west. Grant listened to the clank and jingle that died away in the night. Then he caught the grind of wheels behind him.

Roe cantered up. "Patrol?" he asked.

"A damned poor one," commented Grant. "That officer didn't look at my pass. Where did they come from?"

"Other side of Flushing. Better keep extra sharp watch now." He trotted back toward the chaise.

If there were marauders about, Grant thought, they would have scattered into the night at the sight of the lantern-lit patrol. Now that it had passed, they could resume their operations with reasonable assurance that they would not be interfered with. He rode on, but it was hard to keep awake. The night landscape fogged and blurred, played odd tricks on him. Flushing Village, lightless and sleeping, was passed, with the shimmer of its bay and the thick smell of salt marshes.

Somewhere beyond the village Roe ordered a halt. Grant dismounted, leaning stiffly against his horse while Roe pounded at the door of a darkened inn. Lights showed, fresh horses for the chaise were led out, and the night march went on. The hood of the chaise had been put up and there was no sign or sound from the occupants.

For a while Grant rode behind, then he was in the lead again. To keep awake, he beat his hat against his knee, pinched his eyelids, twisted a strap painfully tight about an arm.

Then ahead on the road, he saw two dark forms, barely distinguishable from the sandy surface. Suddenly he was wide-awake. He bent low in the saddle, staring ahead. Two men. He was sure of that. They stood still now, quite close together, leaning on staves.

He gathered the gray, sent it galloping down on the pair, who drew quickly to the right side of the road. Twenty yards from them, Grant drew his pistols, cocked them and then sent the gray crashing at a sharp angle into a clump of deep bushes to the left. Something flashed in the dark and his horse shied. A man yelled in pain. Half a dozen figures fled across open meadow, the gray hard after them. Grant fired over their heads.

The fugitives seemed to have been swallowed up by the night. Grant swung the gray back to the road. The two men with the staves were nowhere in sight.

When Roe came up, Grant asked, "The ladies all right?"

"They weren't amused. What made you break off the road?"

"I saw two men on ahead of me, too few to have done anything, but I guessed they had some friends hidden close by and those bushes looked the right place for them. Surprise is everything and I figured it was better if I did the surprising."

"Judgmatical," said Roe with a nod of approval. "Why didn't you chase 'em farther?"

"That might have been just what they wanted. Maybe there were still more hiding somewhere. That would have left you alone."

"You don't figure much wrong," said Roe. "Yes, they were after the chaise."

"This chaise? How could they have known about it?"

Roe pushed back his hat. "There it was, waiting at Onderdonk's. Someone could have seen it and passed the word along."

"Do we have to look after it much longer?"

"Some," said Roe. "We're not past Oyster Bay yet."

An hour later Grant was aware of a new smell in the air, the reek of tidal waters mingled with the scent of new-mown hay and a hint of wood smoke. Roe cantered up, pointing ahead where low hills showed dimly against the sky. "See that house, just under the shoulder?"

Grant could just make out a roofline against the sky and some yellow lights. Roe went on, "How many windows would you say are lit?"

Grant cupped his hands about his eyes, concentrating on the yellow sparks. "One — two — I make it four."

Roe gave a sigh of relief. "Four it is. Ride into that field at the left. Six-bar gate a little way in. Tell me how many bars are down. I want to stay here and watch the house."

Beyond surprise, Grant rode into the field; soon he found the high, barred gate which held some mysterious message for Roe. To make certain, he dismounted and ran his hands along each bar. Then he rejoined Roe. "Six-bar gate. The four upper bars were down. Two lowest in place."

Roe rubbed his lean jaw. "Two bars in place. Four lights in the house. Four and two most usually make six. We leave the road right here. We're heading for the sixth inlet on the east shore of Setauket Bay. I'll bring up the chaise. You follow behind."

As they rode along a grassy track that sloped to the east, Grant could hear the slight hiss of waves breaking on sand. Then the bay glimmered dully before him. The chaise halted on the narrow beach. Roe had already dismounted and was walking along the beach out of earshot of the women.

A huge man emerged and started toward Roe, his cloak swinging and his heavy boots crunching on the shingle. Grant reached for his holster but relaxed when Roe called softly, "Caleb." Then a second man, shorter and stouter, obviously a civilian, appeared.

"Is it pressing?" Grant heard him ask Roe.

29

"Desperate." Roe's answer was low, but clear.

The civilian sighed. "I was afraid so, when I heard from 723. Who's with you?"

"Two ladies under safe-conduct. American and British both, as usual. Signed by General Anthony Wayne and Sir Henry Clinton. They're passing into Connecticut."

Grant whistled under his breath. "So they'll cross the Sound with us," he thought. "Maybe I'll get a chance to talk to Laurel a little."

Roe beckoned to him. "This is Grant Ledyard, late of Bland's," he said to the others. "Rejoining the service. Ledyard, meet Abraham Woodhull and this is Captain Caleb Brewster, Continental Artillery."

Grant stared at them in the darkness as he acknowledged the introductions. Woodhull and Brewster, two links in that incredible chain that stretched across the Sound from Robert Townsend sometimes known as Samuel Culper, to Benjamin Tallmadge, sometimes known as John Bolton.

Brewster's deep voice broke in. "Ready?"

"Ready," answered Roe. "Good-by, Ledyard. Keep the pistols. They're yours. Got the saddlebags and Floyd's letter? Good luck to you." The night swallowed up Austin Roe.

Grant stuffed the pistols in his saddlebags with a thrill of possession. They were finer than any weapons he had ever hoped to own. Woodhull stepped to the chaise and handed both women down.

Grant took off his hat. "May I help you with your things? Have you far to go?"

The girl said in a low, grave voice, "We've been obliged to you for your escort. From here we go by boat, sir."

Again the thought of crossing with them gave him an odd pleasure, intensified by his own relief at having finished the most dangerous part of his journey. Not that she had paid much actual attention to him through the long ride. But he had a persistent idea that she had been studying him, as though weighing and measuring him. He started to answer her as if he were before her in full dragoon kit, then remembered that, after all, he was still in enemy territory, where his role of a countryman must be maintained. He began gathering up their luggage, which he could handle easily with his saddlebags. There were two valises, cloth-sided, a small horsehair trunk and a canvas bag. "I'll see these aboard for you, Ma'am." he said.

Brewster called, "This way, then."

With a murmur of thanks to Grant, the women followed the big man along a path that skirted the beach. A whaleboat waited in a narrow inlet. Brewster sprang aboard, then held out a broad hand and helped the woman up the plank. Grant followed, balancing his load carefully.

The girl turned quickly. "You're going across, too?"

"That's my aim."

"But I thought—" She broke off suddenly as she caught sight of the whaleboat's crew grouped in the bow. They wore ragged uniform coats and their muskets, muzzles plugged and locks carefully wrapped, were leaning against the gunwale, near at hand. "You're all soldiers!" she cried in alarm. "And those guns!"

"Continental Army, Ma'am," Brewster said.

Her voice rose higher. "Major Slade said nothing about this. He said we'd go in a trading boat." There was real distress in her tone.

"Likely he didn't know," Brewster said quietly. "But if you tried to cross with civilians in an unarmed boat, you wouldn't like where you ended up. Of course, if you want to step ashore, the liberty's yours."

Unexpectedly she dropped to a cross seat, drawing her companion, who clutched a leather case, with her. "It's all right, Aunt Ann. Once we get across, we'll go where we won't see any more soldiers, royal or rebel."

The older woman sniffed. "Of course it's all right, soldier or trader. My intention's for the other shore, even if I have to paddle myself over on a plank. You just rest here by me, Laurel."

Grant stowed their belongings by their feet and was rewarded with a husky, "Thank you."

Then Brewster beckoned. Grant made his way forward and found the huge man standing by a canvas-hooded swivel gun. "The boys will man this if there's trouble crossing," he said in a low tone. "I'd be glad if you'd act as gun captain."

"Expect trouble?" asked Grant.

"Expect it oftener than I get it. I'll be aft if you want me."

"By the way," said Grant, "be sure not to mention my name or regiment where the women might hear you. The girl doesn't seem to like soldiers."

Brewster grinned. "You're just an extra hand, so far as I'm concerned."

The whaleboat headed north out of Setauket Bay toward the Sound, which was turning to green and gold and purple as the sun edged up in the east. Grant settled himself in the bow and began to speculate on the two women passengers, particularly the girl.

Where had she come from? Since their papers had been signed by Anthony Wayne, their journey must have started in American territory. Wayne must have sent them to the nearest British post from which they had gone to New York, been cleared by Sir Henry's staff and sent on their way. But why? And where were they going? The girl had said, "We're going where we won't see any soldiers, royal or rebel." During the long night ride from Onderdonk's they had witnessed the smooth working of Washington's secret chain of communication on Long Island. How much had they guessed or suspected? Certainly, they had asked no questions and evinced no interest in what went on. They must be safe enough. Yet what accounted for the girl's obvious aversion to uniforms and arms?

Suddenly a voice shouted, "Sail off the port bow!"

32

The whaleboat was bucking a gentle swell. Off to the west, a bright square came into view, dipped and bobbed. Behind him, Grant could hear the rustle of wrappings being torn from musket-locks. Now the sail of a small sloop showed clearer against a wakening sky. From the sloop's bow a puff of smoke welled, followed by a flat report. The plume of white water shot up a good hundred yards short of the whaleboat.

The men at the swivel grunted disparagingly. One of them said, "They'll never close with us on this course."

The hostile boat was making straight for Long Island. The sail began to dance and sway, turned pink. Soon it was barely visible.

III

United States Dragoon

Two hours later Grant blinked in the morning light as a crewman roughly shook him. He tried to gather his thoughts. His last recollection was of a dawnlit sea, empty but for one vanishing sail to port. Now a land breeze, fragrant with the scent of fields and brooks, blew over him. The whaleboat was coasting easily west toward the mainland. To the right he saw a marshy creek mouth, and a low hill faced by a small fort where the colors of the United States floated high.

Then he looked aft. The seat where the girl and her aunt had sat was vacant. In the stern, Brewster held the tiller.

"Where are your passengers?" Grant asked him.

"Put 'em ashore at Black Rock." Brewster jerked a thumb over his shoulder. "That's the real port for Fairfield. But I'm landing you at Fairfield Beach. Get ready to jump when we touch."

Grant looked toward the shore where a few houses, white and silvery gray, shone on a slight rise. "I'd have liked the chance to wish them good luck. Both of them," he remarked as he picked up his saddlebags, making sure that Culper's packages were still in them.

The beach was very close now. A flimsy wharf ran out into the water. Behind it was a broad stretch of sand. The whaleboat grated against the wharf, and Grant sprang onto it. "Where am I supposed to go?" he called to Brewster.

Brewster pointed inland. "Keep going. I'll be along later." The whaleboat pushed off.

As Grant's feet struck the road beyond he forgot his weariness and hunger. For the first time in more than two years, he was walking toward a New England village. He was back in his own part of the world. Approaching the first houses, he saw the walls were smoke-blackened above gaping windows, and that the roofs were sagging. Off to the left, chimneys rose stark like broken teeth from ragged cellarholes. He remembered that Tryon, the former governor of New York, had raided as far inland as Danbury.

When he turned into the main street of Fairfield, he saw that one or two houses had been reshingled and new glass set in the windows. There were trim flower beds. He wondered how these people had the courage to rebuild with the British just across the narrow sound.

Up the main street he saw a rider approaching. As he came nearer, Grant caught a glint of brass and a toss of white plume, and then he could make out epalets on each shoulder. There was no mistaking that easy seat, that assured, alert lift to the head, that long-limbed body with its hint of controlled energy. Grant called, "Major! Major Tallmadge!"

The major reined in, looking down at Grant impatiently. Grant had not seen Tallmadge since the breakup of the Valley Forge camp in '78 and somehow he had expected to find him changed — battered, perhaps, like Fairfield. But the powdered hair was as neat as ever under the brass helmet and the ice-blue eyes under the level brows were still cool and steady. Tallmadge said quickly, "You have business with me, sir? I'm a little pressed for time."

Grant drew closer and dropped his voice. "I've a package for you, sir. From Samuel Culper."

Tallmadge looked keenly down at Grant. "Where's Brewster?"

"He told me he'd see you later."

"You were with him?"

"Yes. He landed me at Fairfield Beach."

With an expert swing, Tallmadge dropped from the saddle, the reins under his arm. "You expect to see Mr. Culper again?" he asked.

35

Grant shook his head. "Not likely. I'm — well, there's no reason why you should remember me. I was senior lieutenant in the second troop of Bland's. My name's Grant Ledyard."

Tallmadge's expression changed as a smile softened his eyes and mouth. "I remember you now. From Massachusetts, aren't you? Weren't you mentioned in orders for annoying some Hessians beyond Valley Forge? How do you happen to be bringing me packages from our friend in New York?"

Grant told of his meeting with Townsend, whom he was careful to call Culper.

Tallmadge threw back his head in a gesture that Grant remembered, one that gave him the appearance of looking from a great height into far distances. "I see. We'd better go to my room at the Oxbow." He started off at a long, easy stride, his horse clopping behind him. As Grant fell into step, the major asked, "Did you have much talk in New York?"

"Enough to know that you'd be anxious to see what I've got."

A sergeant and two troopers lounged on the inn steps. They jumped to attention as Tallmadge strode up. "Burris," he said, "be ready to ride out the instant you have word from me. Sergeant Graves, tend to my door, please." He led Grant up a flight of broad, battered stairs, then along a corridor where he unlocked a door, motioning Grant to enter. Once inside, the major turned the key, leaving the sergeant on guard outside.

Tallmadge tossed his helmet onto the white-testered bed and turned to Grant. "You've seen so much already that it is almost naïve of me to ask for your word that nothing you see or hear will go beyond these walls."

"You have my word," answered Grant. He laid his packages on the gate-legged table and put Colonel Floyd's letter next to them.

Tallmadge unlocked a small cupboard by the fireplace and took out a fine-haired brush and a battered book. "Pull up beside me, Mr. Ledyard," he said, seating himself at the table. "This letter. Yes. To Colonel Floyd." He held the sheet so Grant could read it.

36

Culper's clear script stood out boldly, a simple business letter expressing regret that the Colonel's orders could not be fulfilled at once. There followed a good deal of detail about certain household items with comments on the probable sequence in which they might be received. No wonder the British officers who had seen it had passed it by as harmless. Grant glanced at Tallmadge, whose strong-featured face was impassive. He drew from his pocket a thin vial filled with a colorless liquid, and uncorked it carefully. Without looking at Grant he said, "You must never mention the existence of this liquid to anyone."

With a deft touch he dipped the brush into the liquid and began to flick the point lightly over the letter. As Grant watched, the wet streaks showed dark, faded, and then greenish words began to stand out between the lines of Robert Townsend's apologies to his friend Colonel Floyd. They were meaningless to Grant.

The major ran his fingers about his neck as though loosening his stock, drew out a silver chain, a pencil-like cylinder of metal dangling from it. The top of the cylinder came off with a faint pop and Tallmadge pulled forth tightly rolled papers that he spread beside the letter. The script on the papers was very fine and Grant could only see that it consisted of columns of numbers against which proper names and words were set. A corner of the paper slid toward him and he made out some of the names. 712 was Sir Henry Clinton, British commander; 723 stood against the name of Culper, while 711 was identified simply as G. W.

Grant felt prickles along his spine. He started, roused from useless fear, as the major shouted, "Sergeant Graves!"

The reply came muffled through the door. "Sir?"

"My compliments to Lieutenant Gunnison. He's to alert every trooper at the post."

Tallmadge sat brooding, his chin sunk in his stock and his mouth tight. Then he straightened up. "Now those packages. You've got something to tell me about them?" He reached for the one that contained the writing paper.

37

For an instant, Grant's memory froze, then his mind cleared. "Twenty-five for the pack you've got there," he said. "Thirty-three for this."

Tallmadge deftly broke open the first package, counted off twenty-five sheets, drew out the twenty-sixth. "Will you do the same with the other?" he asked, frowning. "The thirty-fourth sheet, of course." His brush was already playing over the paper and a jumble of words and numerals was slowly materializing. Then he reached for the sheet Grant held out to him. As Grant straightened out the wrappings of the packages, he read the address: *John Bolton, in care of Abraham Woodhull, Setauket.* It must have been on the Woodhull land that Austin Roe had asked Grant to count the bars in a gate, and the house with the four lights showing was probably Abraham Woodhull's. Some combination of the count had told Roe where to find Caleb Brewster and the whale-boat. He tried to visualize the careful planning, carried on in the face of the most acute danger, which allowed this route from New York to Fairfield to function so smoothly.

Tallmadge turned to Grant. "Would you step down to the porch and tell trooper Burris to mount and stay mounted."

Glad of something to do, Grant strode along the corridor and down the stairs of the porch. The trooper was lounging by a bony sorrel. Grant delivered his message and went back up the stairs through an aroma of bread baking which reminded him that he had not eaten since the day before at Onderdonk's.

As he swung to the top step he saw that the nearest door in the corridor was open. Then he jumped back as a half dozen gold pieces rolled erratically into the corridor. Instinctively he knelt and began picking up the coins. There was a low cry of dismay, and he turned quickly toward the open door. The room, through some freak of construction, made a sharp turn to the right, forming a miniature hall just inside the threshold. In that small, carpeted space he saw the pretty girl of the chaise.

Still kneeling, Grant sat back on his heels, one finger resting on

38

a square coin whose center was oddly pierced. He swept up the coin and offered it with the others to the girl. "I think these are all — no — wait a minute. There's one right under the door." He flicked it out with his free hand.

The girl's eyes were dark with alarm. "You — you followed us!" she said huskily, as she dropped to her knees.

He shook his head. "It's you who've followed me."

"You weren't with those men in the boat?"

"With them. But not one of them," he answered, still holding out the coins.

"You were just crossing — as we were?"

"Pretty much. Here — hold out your hand." He dropped a chinking heap into her palm. Down the corridor he heard Graves cough.

Grant got to his feet quickly and held out his hands. "Let me help you up," he said.

She hesitated, then smiled. "Thank you," she said softly. One hand crammed with gold pieces, she caught Grant's wrist with the other and rose gracefully.

Aunt Ann called briskly, "Have you got them all, Laurel? Who's there?"

"It's all right, Aunt Ann," she called. Then she looked at Grant as though she felt she owed him an explanation. "Aunt Ann's leather case broke and — " she made a scattering gesture. "We're taking it to — "

Grant held out both hands in warning. "Steady! Don't tell *anyone* where you're taking that. You ought to have it sewn into your clothes."

Laurel stepped nearer, eyes very sober. "Thank you for your advice. And I am obliged to you for your help." She looked straight at him, and Grant thought there was more than gratitude in her look. Then she closed the door.

Grant rubbed his wrist over his forehead. "Now what the devil! All that gold!"

Sergeant Graves' face was impassive as Grant came toward him. "Go right in, sir. I rapped when I saw you on the stairs and the major unlocked the door."

Grant found Tallmadge making up a neat packet of papers. Pen and ink stood at his elbow on the gate-leg table. "Well?" he asked.

"Burris is mounted and waiting."

"Good," said Tallmadge, smoothing back his powdered hair. His handsome face looked drawn and deep lines showed between his eyes. "This is the devil and all," he went on, tapping the papers. Then his face cleared and he smiled. "Excuse me. I'm talking riddles. I'll explain — that is, if your mind can stand another secret."

"Another?" thought Grant.

"I'll try to answer your questions," Tallmadge went on. "I think I can guess your first one."

Grant grinned at him. "Can you? Well, it's 'When do I eat?'"

Tallmadge pushed back his chair. "That's damned stupid of me. Sergeant Graves! Call the landlord! Breakfast for two. Well, to return to your second question — all this is about the French at Newport."

"The — who?" exclaimed Grant.

"Yes, that's right," said Tallmadge, stretching out his long legs. "A whole army's landing at Newport under Rochambeau. Some are ashore, some still aboard. Their stores, their artillery are in the same shape. They're covered by a very small fleet."

Grant said wearily, "So we're leaning on the French again. Wasn't Savannah enough? They got us into a nasty hole there and then sailed off for the West Indies."

Tallmadge looked keenly at him. "You may judge differently when you hear the whole story. Anyway, there they are at Newport. Now Culper writes that the British are loading thousands of troops off Whitestone, at the west end of Long Island. They're to be sent to Newport to hit the French while they're still unloading."

Grant whistled. The French would be half afloat, half ashore.

Their infantry would be rotten with sea-sickness and scurvy. The predicament was obvious. "What can we do?" he asked.

Tallmadge's face was bleak. "We've got no navy. We couldn't march what army we have overland in time to do any good. And if we did, Clinton would seize the whole Hudson and cut the States in two." He sat up quickly, his expression changing to one of determination. "General Washington will do *something,* though."

Grant nodded. "You'll send on Culper's warning to the Commander?"

"With a strong escort, under Gunnison. I may need Burris here," said Tallmadge, striding to the window, glancing out, turning back again. "There are damn bad people around the Sound. Call them what you like — Skinners and Cowboys, Whig partisans, Tory partisans. They're all alike. Out for plunder, and they don't mind killing to get it. They've snapped up my messengers before. This time I'm taking no chances." He lowered his voice. "Four thousand first-class French troops with guns and cavalry. Rochambeau has put himself unreservedly under Washington. But it will be the end for us if Rochambeau's smashed on the Newport beaches."

"Do we know how many men Clinton's going to throw against the French?"

Tallmadge looked surprised. "Know? Of course. The sheets you brought give a list of every unit, British or Hessian, that's embarking. We know who commands them right down to company level. We know their records in the past, their present state. Every ship is there — armament, tonnage and so on."

Grant thought of Culper in New York, sitting among his books, beaming delightedly at finding himself in such an agreeable world and among such agreeable people. Officers of all ranks sought him out and he listened to them sympathetically, anxious to help them, if he could, by writing about them and their activities for Rivington's *Gazette.* Undoubtedly Culper frequented the coffee houses about Wall Street and William Street. He might share a bottle with a major whose command was being left out of a pending expedition. A line, just a line in the *Gazette* that headquarters would be sure to read. Something complimentary about the major and his men. The major would be hugely obliged if good old Townie could see his way clear — A useful, busy, pleasant life for a smiling, dark-haired man who protested that he was too timid to be a soldier!

Grant looked up, aware that Tallmadge was speaking to him. "I was just saying," remarked the latter, "that I haven't quite finished sealing up these papers. While I do it, would you mind addressing a cover for them? Ready? 'For His Excellency, General George Washington. To be opened in his absence by Colonel Alexander Hamilton, *and by no other hand.*' Got that? Better underscore the last five words."

Package and cover were finished when the sergeant knocked on the door. Tallmadge opened it and Graves set down a big tray where the smoke of coffee blended with that of chops above mounds of potato and bread.

Grant ate ravenously while Tallmadge paced up and down the room. Then hoofs sounded below and Tallmadge caught up the packet and ran out of the room. Grant heard the shuffle and rasp as troopers dismounted, caught Tallmadge's clear voice followed by a mutter of acknowledgment. Someone called, "Prepare to mount! Mount!" and the cavalcade jingled away into the July morning.

Grant looked up as Tallmadge swung into the room, clear-eyed and smiling, his head high. "Well!" exclaimed Grant, turning around to look at him.

"That's a weight off my shoulders," he said. "I've done everything humanly possible about our news. There's nothing for me to do now except wait. Did you get enough to eat?"

"For the moment," said Grant, sopping up a pool of gravy with bread. "When I think of the rations at Charleston . . ."

Tallmadge nodded sympathetically. "I know how you feel. But you didn't miss much by being south last winter. Really, it was worse here than at Valley Forge, something that I didn't think possible."

"Worse?" said Grant sardonically. "You must have forgotten Valley Forge."

"Not I. It was far colder than the Forge. We had more men to look after and fewer rations." He poured himself a glass of rum, sat twisting it idly as he studied Grant. After a couple of sips, he said, "Now how about you, Ledyard? What do you want to do?"

Grant pushed away his plate and a sinking feeling crept over him. "I've been thinking about that — of course. My mind was just about made up that I'd done about all I could. How do I help, for example, by rotting through another fall and winter along the Hudson. It'll be the same story all over."

Tallmadge set down his glass. "What will you do, then?"

Grant frowned. "I'm past twenty-five. Before the war, I was intending for the law. My father had a good practice in Worcester. But if I stay out another year, two years, I'll be too old to start at the bottom of the law ladder."

"It would be hard," agreed Tallmadge. "You went to Harvard, didn't you?"

"Yes, but I left at the end of my sophomore year for the army, so I haven't a degree. That's not essential in law, but it's a big help."

"I find it hard to put myself in your place, Ledyard," observed Tallmadge. "I'd graduated from Yale before this started and was established as a schoolteacher. But — well, I see nothing to hinder your resigning. And you could leave the army knowing that your very last act was your most valuable. I refer, of course, to our New York friend. You've made a most interesting summing up of your problem. There's one thing, though. I noted that you used the past tense in describing your thoughts. Why?"

"I — I've — " He got up quickly. "I've been fooling myself. All the time I've been thinking, 'Just let me get to the American lines. That's all. I'm through.' But I was wrong. In New York I saw one American living in the very heart of the British Army, risking

43

everything for us. Could I resign and go home, knowing about Culper and his work? No! Damned if I could."

Tallmadge nodded approvingly. "Yes. Samuel Culper is a pretty healthy subject to think about when one begins to feel sorry for oneself."

"No doubt about that. Good God, for sheer, raw courage, it beats anything I ever heard of. I only hope that he gets paid accordingly, not that that would make any difference to him."

"Paid?" asked Tallmadge raising his eyebrows. "Oh, yes, of course. Well, as a matter of fact, Ledyard, he won't take a penny, not even for expenses. The Commander and I have had the matter up with him several times. The same goes for Roe and Woodhull, although Woodhull said he might put in a claim for expenses at the end of the war." He balanced a pen between his long fingers. "So you'll stay. I thought you would. Now for your future. There isn't much of your old regiment left. Suppose I arrange to transfer you to my command, the 2nd Dragoons." He turned, looked out the window into the sunlit world of Fairfield. "You would work with me here. How about it?"

Grant started. "With you? Here? On the Culper business?"

"Why not?"

"But it's quite out of my line. I've been staff and line, not work like this. Besides, are you sure you want me? You can't know a great deal about me."

Tallmadge smiled tolerantly. "My dear Ledyard, I'm afraid you don't give me credit for powers of observation. After all, there aren't many cavalry officers in our army. I could give you a pretty complete dossier of any of them, I think. I've watched you in the field, particularly in the Valley Forge patrols. I've heard about you at headquarters and from your superiors. Everything points to your being known as a steady, resourceful officer who can fit in most anywhere. You make up your mind quickly and aren't afraid to act. I could cite a little collision you and your men had with some Hessians along the Schuylkill and another along the Delaware. No,

44

I'm not acting blindly. So shall I make the proper arrangements?"

Grant looked keenly at him. Then he said, "I'll be proud to serve under you, sir."

"Then that's settled. Elisha Sheldon's our colonel, but I have a free hand in matters like this from the Commander. There'll be no difficulty about the transfer. Then there's another point, Ledyard. I remember that you speak French."

Grant nodded. "A Canadian refugee settled in Worcester and taught me French to amuse himself. I'm pretty rusty, of course, but it would come back to me."

"Good. You see, if Rochambeau's army survives at Newport, we'll be right on the line of communication between him and the Commander. A French-speaking American officer would be invaluable." Tallmadge picked up his helmet. "I've got to go out for a while. The room's yours."

"Just a minute," said Grant. "How about the — " he made brushing motions over a sheet of paper.

Tallmadge smiled. "I stowed the codes and the rest of the stuff away while you were eating. Why don't you get some sleep." He waved as he left the room.

Grant slipped off his coat, bent to unfasten his shoes. There was a rap at the door. "That you, sergeant?" called Grant.

A sad voice answered, "It's me. The landlord. Mr. Moobie."

Grant flung open the door and saw a round-faced man with moist, prominent eyes set above puffy cheeks.

"The ladies in Room Five would be glad of a word with you. They're in the parlor, just to the left of the foot of the stairs."

Grant pulled on his coat, refastened his shoe buckles. "Do you know what they want?"

Mr. Moobie folded his hands under his striped apron. "Oh, yes indeed. They want a word with you."

Grant followed him down the stairs. "Here's the door, sir," said the landlord. "You may go in."

The girl had changed to a sea-green dress and her golden

45

hair was carefully arranged. Grant bowed to her, and turned to her aunt who was sitting in a deep chair by the window. "Your servant, Ma'am," he said, looking at her with interest. He noticed her pleasant, rather angular face under a mass of silvery hair. Her hands, folded calmly in her lap, were strong and well shaped.

"It is good of you, young man, to take the trouble to come down here," she said. "May I ask your name?"

Grant named himself, including the girl in his bow.

"And I am Mrs. James Delmar. Widow. This is my niece, Laurel Dane," she said briskly. "Do sit down."

He drew up a chair facing the two women. The withdrawn look had gone from Laurel Dane's face and he thought she looked at him with interest. He shifted his chair a little so that he could watch Laurel unostentatiously out of the corner of his eye. Mrs. Delmar went on, "Laurel and I expected to be met here, but instead we found a letter waiting for us. We have had to arrange for a chaise through our landlord, but the roads, even in daylight, are not safe. And, as you know, we have a few gold pieces."

"Yes," said Grant. "But as I pointed out to Miss Dane, it is not wise to mention such possessions."

Laurel spoke for the first time. "What we hope is that we may persuade you to ride the rest of the way with us as a guard."

Grant checked an involuntary whistle of surprise. "Excuse me, Miss Dane, but you seem to be dangerously trustful."

Mrs. Delmar looked squarely at him. "We have talked this over thoroughly, young man, and we have already made up our minds."

Laurel broke in hastily, "We know it's a great deal to ask. Of course, we'd want to pay you for your time."

"No need of that," protested Grant. "But why not ask the local authorities for an escort of troopers."

Laurel cried out, "No. We don't want soldiers."

He looked at her in surprise, then remembered her distaste for men in uniform. Dubiously he said, "I still don't see why you trust me, a total stranger."

"Call it woman's intuition, Mr. Ledyard," said Mrs. Delmar firmly. "You inspire trust, therefore you can be trusted. Not that I think you're any saint, but that's beside the point. We want a shield, not a halo."

He caught a look of amusement in the girl's eyes as she said, "I hope you'll say yes, Mr. Ledyard."

"How far is it?" asked Grant.

Mrs. Delmar cocked her head, underlip caught between her teeth. "H'm — five, no call it six and a half miles. Just as far as the Aspetuck. You know where that is, I suppose."

Grant shook his head. "I don't know the country about here well."

"Aunt Ann does," Laurel put in quickly. "You can get a saddle horse from Mr. Moobie."

Fourteen miles at the most for the round trip, Grant mused. And Tallmadge would not be back till sundown, so he could leave with a clear mind. He got to his feet. "When do you want to start?"

Laurel cried, "You will go?"

"It's a bargain," said Grant, and half seriously held out his hand.

To his surprise she rose in a graceful swirl of green skirts and placed her hand in his. "A bargain, Mr. Ledyard — but all on our side, I'm afraid. Do you mind if we start now?"

Grant smiled at her. "You're quite ready?"

"Our things are all in the chaise."

"Then I'll go up and get my saddlebags. My pistols are in them. I'll see Moobie about the animal when I come down."

"The animal? Oh, your horse?" She looked at him mischievously. "You won't have to see Mr. Moobie. I've told him you'd want one. It's waiting for you."

Upstairs, after he had carefully reloaded the English pistols and stowed them in his saddlebags, Grant looked at himself in the mirror over the mantel. "You must look like a bleating innocent to the rest of the world. Culper sends you over his secret road. Tallmadge lets you watch a code being unraveled. Now two strange women ask you to escort them and their gold over a dangerous route. Oh, well — " He turned and went downstairs.

In the stable yard he found Laurel and Mrs. Delmar already seated in a rickety chaise, the latter holding the reins in one competent hand. By the wheel, Mr. Nangle, a lanky, cadaverous man with a long, sour face was serving them with wine. "There's a glass for you, Mr. Ledyard," Mrs. Delmar called. Laurel smiled at him.

Grant raised his glass with a bow, drank it off and then fastened his saddlebags to the broad-beamed horse that Mr. Moobie must have taken from a plow hitch. Without waiting for him, Mrs. Delmar started the chaise out into the sun-dappled main street, and he urged his horse into a lumbering trot, careful to keep a few paces distance between the chaise and himself. It seemed unwise to advertise that Mrs. Delmar had engaged an escort for a journey in broad daylight.

As he rode on, Grant watched the country unfold before him. White houses and solid red barns basked in the sun as the land rose in a series of green shoulders, shaggy with oak and maple and chestnut and pine. Cattle lurched deliberately across rocky pasture land. Broad cornfields dipped and rustled to the breeze. Soft and brown, the road stretched on, twisting lazily about a round hill, dipping into shady hollows where dragonflies darted over still pools, climbing again between stone walls and pasture fences. Then suddenly it seemed to Grant that men in the fields turned inquiringly as the chaise went by.

Why did that man among the beanpoles lean on his hoe and watch so keenly? Off to the left a plowman checked his team and called, waving to someone farther along. He was answered by a man high up the hill, who looked down at the road and then pointed into the distance. Grant was uneasy. He set his horse into a trot and pulled up by the chaise. Laurel seemed fast asleep, her head thrown back on the shabby cushioning, and a faint line showing between her eyes as though her unconscious thoughts were

48

troubled. Mrs. Delmar spoke crisply. "Well, young man, I was beginning to wonder just who was escorting whom." He hastily explained his reason for staying well in the rear, and she nodded. "I ought to have figured that out for myself. Things seem quiet enough, but you never can tell. I'd hate to have anything happen when we're so close to the end."

"You've had a long journey?" Grant ventured.

"Quite," said Mrs. Delmar with a flick of the reins.

Grant flushed. "I assure you I wasn't prying."

"Stuff!" exclaimed Mrs. Delmar. "Of course you weren't. But you've been wondering. This trip started months ago. I was here." She dropped her voice and Grant bent to catch her words over the grind of the wheels. "My niece was in the west. After her parents were killed, it was thought best that she come here. The mails take a long time, but I finally arranged to meet her in the Jerseys."

"The Jerseys? Where'd she been? Pennsylvania?"

"No one will know just where until the boundaries are better settled. It might have been there, or in lower New York."

Grant thought of the massacres in the Wyoming Valley, in Cherry Valley in '78, of John Sullivan's expedition up the Susquehanna and the retaliations that followed that raid. The district was one any civilian would want to leave. But when he tried to map out a logical escape route, the story began to puzzle him. He asked, "Why didn't she simply come east to the Hudson? You'd have been in the zone of just one army. As it is, you've gone from rebel to British and back to rebel again."

"And a niggling business it was, what with passes and signatures and countersignatures," said Mrs. Delmar with an angry sniff. "But there were property matters that had to be settled. Land and houses on Staten Island." She gave a brisk toss of her head. "These young people! I've handled my own affairs for years and I thought I could help Laurel over the last steps of all this business of deeds and assignments, but she went out early one morning, all by herself and when she came back to where we were staying, there was the gold in a leather case under her arm."

Grant nodded to himself. All that accounted for the gold. He glanced at Laurel, still asleep beside her aunt. Was she asleep? It seemed to him that her mouth had tightened slightly as the older woman talked on, as though she were displeased by the account. Of course she was asleep and no wonder, after that long trip. He raised his hand to Mrs. Delmar, told her that he was going to ride ahead and scout out the road.

When he reached the foot of a steep dip where the road crossed a stream, he waited until the chaise loomed at the crest and began its descent. There was thick undergrowth at both ends of the log bridge, dense, mosquito-filled clumps. Laurel was driving, expertly keeping a slanting course to minimize the steep grade. As she came nearer, he saw that a brace of pistols lay between her and her aunt. He called reassuringly to her, was answered by a confident wave, then started out again.

The road ran straight with wide fields on either side. He urged his lamentable horse into a gallop toward distant treetops that must mask another steep, sudden drop. Then he was among the trees, looking down at a second log bridge and the "S" of the road climbing beyond it. All at once his horse shied. Grant dropped the reins, whipped out his pistols, dismounting, made his way cautiously along the side of the road. The hollow lay hot and silent before him. Twice he started, thinking that he had caught the glint of a musket barrel in the bushes, but each time it turned out to be the sun striking on round, smooth wood. He worked his way across the bridge, bridle over his arm, and began the ascent on the other side. At the far crest, he stopped and wiped his forehead. "Blast it, I need more practice in scouting," he muttered. "There's nothing here. I'm just too damned jumpy."

There were more little streams and more hills, occasional farms. And always the chaise followed along in Grant's wake. At last he halted on a high shoulder that looked to the west. Before him, thrown into sharp relief by the growing slant of the sun, ran a long, ravinelike valley. A good two hundred feet below him a stream slid south, long stretches of calm, dark water alternating with sudden white ruffles where black rocks jutted. Just below him a rambling white house nestled into a wide shelf, barns and outhouses spreading away to the left. A curving drive reached up to join the road.

A group of men appeared on the porch, three of them dressed for travel. The fourth, short and stout in Quakerlike clothes, waved a low-crowned hat to them as they mounted tethered horses and rode away to the south.

Grant turned to see Laurel looking at house and valley with a rapt expression. "The valley!" she cried. "Aunt Ann, it's just the same."

"It's the same," said her aunt dryly. "Times aren't."

Laurel shook her brown curls. "Look! That must be Uncle Jethro. Call to him!" She flicked the reins and sent the horse ambling toward the drive.

Grant followed. His easy mission was done and he was free to return to Fairfield and map out his future with Benjamin Tallmadge. Yet he wanted to linger.

The stout man came briskly down the steps with his arms outstretched and Laurel sprang to the ground and ran toward him. Grant caught a jumble of words.

"Well, well! My little niece! Home at last!" . . . "So happy to be here, Uncle Jethro. . . . "

Mrs. Delmar spoke crisply to Grant. "Journey's end, young man, and you needn't look so downcast about it. The Aspetuck Valley won't run away and neither shall we. Come along and let me present you to my brother-in-law."

By the steps, the stout man was patting Laurel's shoulder and Grant felt a little awkward about breaking in on such an intimate scene: the reunion between uncle and niece. As he came nearer, he thought he caught a murmured, "So everything's all right?"

from Mr. Hollis and a hurried, "Yes, but we'll talk later," from Laurel.

The pair stepped apart as Mrs. Delmar presented Grant. Hollis's broad, rather plain face lit up as Grant acknowledged the introduction. "Bless my soul! I didn't know about this! Another helper for us. Capital! We can — "

The sharpness of Laurel's voice surprised Grant as she said, "Mr. Ledyard volunteered to escort us from Fairfield. He's going to live there."

Hollis gave a short cough. "Exactly! Fairfield! H'm. Of course he can help. Mr. Ledyard, I'm a member of the Connecticut Assembly and I assure you that our body needs all the support we may rally. I'll count on you as on all true men in the state."

"The Assembly, sir?" said Grant. "You hold an honored position."

"I am honored to hold that position," said Mr. Hollis. "There's little I can do to return your kindness, but if ever I can serve you, I shall be pleased. Now Ann, my dear," he went on, turning to Mrs. Delmar, "your house has been well tended in your absence and the room is ready for our Laurel." He gestured up the hill and Grant saw a smaller replica of the Hollis house, nestling under a shoulder a little to the south.

Laurel looked gravely up at Grant. "I do hope you know how much I appreciate your coming so far with us," she said as she laid her hand in his.

He stammered, "I — why there's nothing to thank me for. The ride was most pleasant. But may I call after you're settled?"

She gently freed her hand. "You'll always be welcome," she said, and her aunt nodded emphatically.

Mr. Hollis rubbed his hands. "Here, here! Bless me, what am I thinking of? A snack for you, Mr. Ledyard, and something in a glass."

"That's thoughtful of you, Mr. Hollis, but I'd best be getting on. How about the chaise?"

"One of my men will take it in to Moobie tomorrow, and — I declare! Here's Rosa, just in time!"

A small, slender girl, vivid red hair streaming in the wind, galloped over the fields on a fine-limbed bay, took a low wall deftly, pulled up by the steps and swung to the ground in a flurry of blue riding habit. Her blue eyes sparkled in a tilt-nosed, pixielike face. "Why, Cousin Laurel!" she cried as she threw her arms about Laurel. Then her restless eyes fell on Grant. "And who — Laurel, dear, aren't you just a little slow in introducing — " Laurel made the introduction. Rosa smiled, "We'll see you here again, I hope, Mr. Ledyard." Somehow there was a tacit assumption of intimacy in her tone, a suggestion that to her Grant was important. He felt pleasantly flattered until out of the corner of his eye, he saw a look of quiet amusement on Laurel's face.

"I have permission to call on Mrs. Delmar and Miss Dane. I shall be most happy if you are about."

Rosa looked at him impishly. "Oh, *I'll* be here," she said.

Hollis patted her cheek. "To be sure she will. This little chick of mine flies about a lot, but she always heads back to her family."

The amused look on Laurel's face deepened. "It'll be good for all of us to have her about." She smiled at her cousin as though Rosa was a gregariously playful kitten. Then she turned a quite different smile on Grant, a look that recalled the first real glimpse of her that he had had outside Onderdonk's. "Once more, do come and see us, Mr. Ledyard. We're under debt to you, but you'd be welcome even without that."

Grant bowed over her hand. "You're very good Miss Dane. I'll pay my respects as soon as I may." He took his leave of Mrs. Delmar, of Jethro Hollis and Rosa. As he mounted and topped the rise beyond the Hollis lands, he looked back. Laurel and her uncle were walking toward the big house in deep conversation. Mrs. Hollis moved briskly beside them while Rosa brought up the rear, her head haughty as though she by no means appreciated the role of

53

amusing pet which her father and her cousin had assigned her before the stranger from Fairfield.

The road back to the Sound flowed smoothly under his horse's hoofs. Soon Greenfield Hill rose at his left and Grant could just see the water, where two British sloops were tacking east, their gun-ports open. A mile or more behind them, a heavier vessel, its sails catching the sun, slid through the calm waters. East. In that direction lay Newport and the French transports. More British ships might glide east in the night, unobserved. The French, Culper had written, were defenseless. He shivered a little at the thought. How could the Commander help them?

There was more life in Fairfield as Grant rode back into the town. Wagons were creaking off toward Black Rock, laden with hides, lumber, casks of vinegar. A patched-up blacksmith's shop near the Oxbow rang with an endless clink-clank, and beyond it a shoemaker had moved his bench under the shade of a great elm. Grant stabled his horse and walked slowly toward the front of the inn. He looked up at the sound of hoofs in the street and saw Tallmadge, eyes on the horizon, cantering into town followed by a lone trooper. The major waved pleasantly. "Hello, Ledyard. Been amusing yourself?"

"You might call it that," answered Grant. "Look here, do you know a man named Hollis up the Aspetuck?"

Tallmadge looked surprised. "Up the Aspetuck? Why yes. That must be old Jethro Hollis. He's a well-known West India trader and landholder. He's served in the Continental Congress as an alternate or whatever you call it. Now he's doing some fine work, they say, in the Connecticut Assembly, trying to straighten out currency snarls. How'd you happen to run into him?"

Grant described his knight-errantry while Tallmadge nodded in approval. "Hollis is a pretty good man to know, I guess. You did well to go along with the ladies. That road can be bad. What did you say the girl's name was? Laurel Dane. H'm. I seem to remember hearing that one of the Hollis girls married a man by that name. He had land grants in the west. So Laurel must be the daughter. Damn it, she's well out of that part of the country."

"But how about where she is now?" asked Grant.

"The lower Aspetuck? That's off the beaten track and it's usually pretty safe. But I tell you, Ledyard, Westchester County and parts of Fairfield are sheer, bloody, senseless murder."

Grant nodded. "And that's why you sent a strong escort with Culper's news?"

"Just why," said Tallmadge grimly. "I've had small patrols butchered before."

"When do you expect to hear what steps the Commander will take?"

Tallmadge shrugged. "In due course. In the meantime, we wait. Now come along. Mr. Moobie has a huge roast of beef that ought to cut like an overboiled potato."

I V

The Beacons

GRANT slept heavily through the night and well into the following morning. When the sun, striking full into the small, neat room that Mr. Moobie had assigned him, made further sleep impossible, he rose, shaved and struggled into the clothes that Robert Townsend had given him in New York. Down the corridor, Tallmadge's door stood open and Grant heard the major's cheery hail as the latter sighted him. "I've breakfast for you here, Ledyard. Eggs, bread, butter and some really quite good tea. Draw up a chair. We'll talk afterwards."

Grant seated himself at the table in the major's room and ate hungrily. Tallmadge stood looking out of the window, head thrown back and chin high. Grant watched him thinking that in many men the whole pose would have suggested arrogance. With Tallmadge it gave an effect of quiet, farseeing alertness.

At last Grant asked, "Any news?"

Tallmadge turned with a quick smile and closed the door. "Yes. The papers got through. Hamilton — that's Alexander Hamilton, you know — was able to overtake LaFayette with a summary of what Culper wrote. LaFayette will warn Rochambeau when he sees him. There's no sign of major British movement yet, but the embarkations at Whitestone are still going on. Incidentally, you must have a lot of back pay coming to you." He grinned at Grant. "Of course, you'll never get it — or much of it. But draw on me, as your superior, for what you need here in Fairfield, within reason."

56

"That's damn good of you," said Grant. "I don't own as much as a chipped farthing. But about the army. Any hint of what the Commander will do?"

Tallmadge shook his head. "Only that we've orders to stand by." He stepped to the table and handed Grant a sheet of paper. "Here's your transfer to the 2nd, all in order. You may be interested to note that it gives you the rank of captain."

"Captain!" exclaimed Grant. "I — well — that's more than I expected, really. My most sincere thanks to you."

Tallmadge waved his hand. "You've earned it and I'll guarantee that you'll have plenty of chance to keep on earning it. You're posted to the 4th Troop, but you know what cavalry's like with us. The men just melt away if you haven't got horses for them, and we're terribly short. At the moment the 4th Troop consists of yourself and one tone-deaf bugler. But I didn't want you for duty with troops anyway. The first thing I'm going to do, and you'll help with it, is to establish a chain of cavalry posts from New London straight west to Stamford. They'll help out communications with the French."

"Assuming that the French survive," said Grant grimly.

Tallmadge threw back his head. "They've got to! I don't know what the Commander will do to help them, but it will be something. In the meantime, I've got to see about a horse and a uniform for you."

Grant laughed ruefully. "A horse? I wish you could get me that gray that I rode across Long Island with Austin Roe."

Tallmadge laughed softly. "Maybe you'd like to dicker with the owner," he suggested. "That gray — it must have been the same one — is owned by a gentleman from Virginia. George Washington by name."

Grant started. "The Commander?"

"No other. He keeps one horse at Onderdonk's and one in Manhattan. Pays for them out of his allowance, for emergencies like yours — or more serious ones. He's had them there for years,

57

and the one in New York is stabled along with Sir Henry Clinton's. The nominal owner we both know."

Grant smiled. "Must be the man who often writes articles for Rivington's *Gazette*."

"Yes," said Tallmadge distractedly. "Hello! What's happening out there?" He stepped to the window and Grant, pushing away his tray, joined him. A dragoon, his face dappled with sweat and dust, was pulling up on a spent horse. Grant saw Sergeant Graves take a white packet from him.

Tallmadge stepped across the room with his swinging gait as Graves appeared. "Any spoken message, sergeant?" he asked, taking the packet.

"None, sir. Just this."

The sergeant left and Tallmadge, closing the door, broke open the seals. Quickly he crossed to the table, drew out the vial and brush and dusted the liquid over the paper. Grant watched Tallmadge's face but there was nothing to be read from it. The letter was only a half-sheet, and the hidden writing could not have consisted of many lines. Yet the major sat there as though considering a lengthy report.

Finally he rose, got out a tinderbox and carefully burned the letter in the fireplace, crumbling the ashes between his fingers. His face still a mask, he said briefly, "Routine. I'll have to be out for a while. Better meet me here in the afternoon."

Left to himself, Grant felt at a loss. He strolled out into the stable yard and thence down a side road that led across the green flats to the beach. The change in Tallmadge's manner disturbed him. Routine matters were not likely to send a man like the major into a mood of deep abstraction. Both the packet and the covering letter had been brought by a dragoon and so were not likely to have come from Culper.

When Grant reached the broad, flat beach, the tide was out and a strong kelpy smell rose from the rocks along the shore. Alongside the rickety wharf he saw a whaleboat. A huge man sprang aboard

58

and grasped the tiller as the boat pushed out into the Sound. Grant called, "Brewster! Caleb Brewster!"

From the stern, Brewster waved at him, but the whaleboat worked steadily out. Was there any connection, Grant wondered, between Brewster's hurried departure and Tallmadge's recent behavior?

He returned to the inn and idled about uneasily. At mid-afternoon he heard hoofbeats. His depression lifted at once. Tallmadge was riding up to the hitching rail, his expression serene. "Hello Ledyard!" he called as he dismounted. "Come into the tap. I want a drink." He led the way into the taproom as his horse, unguided, made its way into the stable yard.

Mr. Nangle grudgingly served them with West India rum and then stalked off to the inner vastnesses of the inn. Tallmadge raised his mug. "To the thirteen states and our allies." Grant drank in response and the major went on, "You know, I'm very glad that you had that ride the other day."

"To the Aspetuck? Why?"

"Because it gave you some idea of the back country."

Tallmadge sipped his rum and set the mug down with a light thud. "Besides, it was a good thing to do. Hollis won't forget that you served as voluntary escort. Then think of the women. They must have felt a lot safer, knowing that they had an American officer with them, even if he wasn't in uniform."

"But they didn't know about me," Grant said.

Tallmadge looked surprised. "You didn't tell them? Why not, in God's name?"

"For a good many reasons, partly intuition if you like. Not knowing much about them, why should I tell them that an American officer met them at Onderdonk's, deep in British territory?"

"True," said Tallmadge. "But if you see them again, they'll be bound to know."

"Time will blur a lot of things," answered Grant. "I certainly hope that I'll see Laurel — I mean both of them — again. When they see me in uniform, that won't tell them I was a soldier at Onderdonk's. They may think that I landed here, a civilian, and that you persuaded me to take service with you."

"Yes," agreed Tallmadge. "They might think that."

"I'd another reason too," Grant went on. "Miss Dane, in particular, seemed to shy away from the sight of a uniform."

The major looked thoughtful. "How do you feel now? Pretty well rested?"

"Good as ever. I only wish there were something for me to do."

Tallmadge nodded. "Well, it's hardly officer's duty, but would you like to take a ride for me?"

"Glad to. Where?"

"Not very far. I was going to wait for a trooper to come in, but if you don't mind, it'll give him a chance to rest. I've been using them all pretty hard lately."

"Tell me about it."

Tallmadge drew out pencil and paper. "This will take you over part of the same route you traveled before." He began to sketch rapidly. "Here's Fairfield. This is the road you know, running on past Greenfield Hill."

"Isn't there a light-infantry post on it?" asked Grant.

"Yes. You go on past Greenfield Hill, but here you turn to the west instead of keeping on north and northwest as you did that other time. Follow this road until you come to the junction of the Aspetuck and the Saugatuck. There's a swampy patch from here — " he prodded with his pencil " — to where the streams join. Cross this little bridge and you'll find high land, just above the fork, leading to the junction. We have a post there, under Lieutenant Gunnison. Is all this clear?"

"I think so," said Grant, frowning over the sketch. "What do I do when I get there?"

Tallmadge drew a packet from his pocket, squarer and thinner than the one Grant had seen that morning. "Give this to Gunnison.

He'll know what to do with it and tell him to send it on to Colonel Sheldon."

"Why don't I go right through to Sheldon?"

"The route's pretty complicated from there on. A road may be safe one night and deadly the next. Gunnison will know about all that." He handed Grant the packet.

"When do you want me to start?"

"About sundown."

Then Tallmadge settled easily back in his chair, talking on as though whiling away a pleasant summer afternoon. He told Grant how disappointed he had been when he had failed to win the Dean's Bounty at Yale in his senior year. He had wanted to do postgraduate work. Instead he had gone to Wethersfield, below Hartford, as a schoolmaster. His dearest friend, Nathan Hale — Grant saw the strong face contract slightly as the name was mentioned — had a teaching post over in East Haddam. In Wethersfield, Tallmadge had known the Deanes. Of course Grant had heard of Silas Deane, who had been in Paris with Ben Franklin. Then there were the Webbs and the Chesters, capital people all of them. Dan Chester had become a colonel very quickly and Tallmadge had held his first commission under him in the Connecticut line. That had been in June of '76. Who would have thought then that the summer of '80 would see the war still trundling on? Oh, it would end someday. And then? Frankly, he couldn't face teaching again, but he was exploring various business ventures with the Webbs. He hoped to be able to take up his father's old estate in Setauket and —

"His estate where?" broke in Grant. "I always thought you were from Connecticut."

Tallmadge smiled. "No, my father, Yale '47, had a parish on Long Island."

Grant's mind was busy as the major talked on about early days on the north shore. He had wondered just why the Commander had detailed a first-rate cavalryman like Tallmadge to such unusual work. Now the reason was clear. Tallmadge would know every name and every spot along the secret road that led from Culper to the Commander, and such knowledge would triple his value. He asked idly, "Brewster's an old Massachusetts Bay name. I suppose Caleb's from there?"

Tallmadge looked innocently at him. "From where?"

"Setauket."

"Ah, so you guessed that? Yes, he is. And he knows every creek mouth and backwater from Gardiner's Bay to Whitestone. He's descended from old Elder Brewster of the Plymouth Colony."

Grant nodded slowly. Sitting there in the cool dimness of the taproom, that secret road across Long Island and the Sound seemed almost unreal. He felt far from wars and uniforms and orders as he listened to the quiet charm of Tallmadge's talk.

At last Tallmadge's chair scraped gently. "About time for you to go, I'm afraid." Those simple words recalled Grant to the present, to the year 1780. Together they strolled out onto the porch where a trooper suddenly materialized, leading a black horse.

Grant tapped his pocket to make sure that the packet was secure, then mounted. Tallmadge raised his hand in farewell. "My regards to Gunnison. Come back by whatever route suits you."

The black gave evidence of a very fair turn of speed as Grant rode north out of Fairfield, so he gave her her head, hoping to reach the turnoff that led to the Aspetuck-Saugatuck junction while it was still light. His mind weighed time and distance, as the mare eased her pace up rolling inclines and picked her way cleverly down the reverse slopes. As he rode on, Tallmadge's last words lingered pleasantly in his mind. He could choose his own route home. After leaving Gunnison, he could keep on up the east bank of the river just on the chance that there might be lights burning in Jethro Hollis's houses. If the windows still glowed in the little house under the high shoulder, it would probably be early enough to stop and pay his respects.

Greenfield Hill was fading in the rear, a somber, purple shadow.

The narrow valleys into which he dipped were growing darker and the evening air was filled with a blending of the scents of brooks and ferns and wet rocks and deep beds of pine needles hidden on the slopes.

On a level stretch where the smell of hay was strong from dusk-shrouded meadows, he saw a gap in the stone wall that lined a field, a gap through which ran what looked like a swamp. This must be the turning that Tallmadge had marked on his map. When Grant estimated the time that had elapsed since he left Fairfield, he was convinced.

So the most important part of the trip was done and he had reached the turnoff while enough light held. The rest would be a steady jog until he was halted by Gunnison's pickets at the river junction.

He crossed a small bridge and set the mare up a steep slope on the other side. The crest was topped by sentinel-like pines. Ahead in the darkness he heard a stifled sound as though someone had suddenly muffled a whinnying horse. His black answered and Grant was suddenly tense in the saddle. He peered into the night. Then he heard the clink of a hoof against a stone, a rattle, the sound of more hoofs. He called sharply, "Who's there?" and reached for the nigh holster. A shock like icy water struck him. The holster was empty, as was its mate on the other side. Again he called, "Who's there?"

A rather sleepy voice answered, "A simple citizen minding his own business. Suppose you mind yours."

Grant relaxed a little. "Which way are you heading? I can't see. We don't want a collision in this flume." Mentally, he cursed the trooper who had not seen to the holsters.

A second voice, that carried a hint of excitement, answered, "We're heading west."

"Then keep on going. So am I. I don't want to ride up your back," called Grant.

The same voice called, "It's all right, boys. He's heading west."

63

As though the words had been a signal, something rustled through the air from the rocky wall at the right and a heavy body crashed into Grant. Arms lashed about him, wrestled him from the saddle and he hit the ground with stunning force. He struggled madly, felt a jarring smash on the back of his head, felt the bite of harsh rope about his arms and legs. Another blow on his head and Grant drifted off into a weird space halfway between consciousness and unconsciousness. He felt detached, merely watching what happened. A man knelt over him and thrust a hard hand into the very pocket where Tallmadge's packet lay. Voices blurred in the ravine. "Got it, by God . . . Look to those knots, Darby. Keep him flat." . . . "Right in that same pocket, like Abner said!" . . . "See what else he's got. Maybe money in his shoes!" "That horse is mine. Jemmy had the last one!" . . . a hand slapped hard across Grant's face and brought lights flashing in his brain. Then a shrill, high voice, carrying a note of command: "Never mind the money! Tighten the ropes, take his horse and let's be off! We've got what we came for!" Hoofs clattered off into the night.

Slowly Grant struggled back to full consciousness. He lay in his bonds with a feeling of death in his heart. The papers were gone, and the man who had taken them had known exactly where to find them. Had he and Tallmadge been overheard, sitting there by the window of the inn? Was one of Tallmadge's troopers in British pay?

Then he started to work on his bonds. They were tough and well tied and it took a good thirty minutes of straining and struggling. Stiffly he got to his feet, trying to recall the sequence of events. What about that hard, high voice that he had heard? A recollection hung in the back of his mind, just out of reach. With a groan he shook himself and started out on the long, weary trail back to Fairfield, his first mission for Tallmadge a black failure.

The sun was well up in the sky when he finally reached the little seaside town and the low porch of the Oxbow. He dreaded facing the major, dreaded telling him that his papers were gone, that he had allowed himself to ride into a trap like a militia recruit.

Tallmadge, bent over a mass of papers at his table, looked up as Grant entered. "You've seen Gunnison?" he snapped, his ice-blue eyes playing over Grant.

Grant answered, "No!"

Tallmadge came a step nearer. "Something happened! What was it?"

Grant found it hard to meet the major's eyes. "I never got there," he answered dully.

Tallmadge's face was set. "The packet! But never mind that now. Come with me!"

Grant followed him out of the room and out into the street where Tallmadge struck toward the beaches at a rapid pace. When they were at the spot where grass gave way to sand, Tallmadge turned to him. "What happened? Keep your voice low."

Grant answered defiantly. "The packet was taken from me."

"Where did this happen?"

"I don't know. It was in the dark and—"

Tallmadge shook him by the arm. "Guess. As closely as you can."

"About two miles from the place where I turned off the north road. I'd crossed a brook and the trail led up the other side through a ravine. There were people ahead of me. I challenged. Then someone jumped me from the top of the ravine wall and threw me out of the saddle. Some others — I don't know how many, joined in. They bound me. They seemed to know exactly what they wanted. They reached right into the pocket where the letter was. After that they searched me for loot. But the packet came first. I had no chance to fight back."

"The ravine!" said Tallmadge quickly. "Yes. I know the one you mean. Did you hear any names?"

"It was all pretty confused. There was someone called Darby. I heard the names Jemmy and Abner."

Tallmadge gave a great sigh of relief. "Then that's all right. Thank God!"

"All right?" Grant's voice cracked in surprise. Then with a shock, understanding crept into his mind. "You mean — you *knew* I'd be attacked on the way?"

Tallmadge shook his head. "No. I hoped. Or rather I gambled."

"You — sent me out there, blind?"

"It was the only way. The letter and packet that came this morning were from the Commander. The packet had false orders for a movement in force by us against Manhattan. The letter told me to see to it that those false orders reached the British. Now I know that they will. If it's in time, Clinton won't dare leave Manhattan to move against the French in Newport."

"Why didn't you tell me?" cried Grant indignantly.

"If you'd known that those orders were supposed to have been captured, you couldn't have acted convincingly. As it was, I can see that you put up such a fight before they tied you that the people who jumped you haven't the least idea we wanted them to succeed."

"I suppose you're right," said Grant, slowly. "Yes, it's possible that I would have eased off a little, tried to save myself as much as I could as soon as they had me. Just the same, it was an awful gamble. Suppose I had ridden right through?"

"Knowing the Commander, I imagine other packets were sent out tonight. I had no idea how I was going to get that packet to the enemy convincingly. Then I heard that a certain group of men not at all friendly to us, would be out tonight. So I passed you the packet openly at the tap. When you left, I saw you off from the porch. So did a good many others."

Grant shook his head. "Why would they think anything of that?"

"They think I'm rather cleverer than I am," said Tallmadge. "They know I have few troopers at my disposal, and that they've been overworked lately. They see me send you off, openly, having previously seen the passage of the packet. They say to themselves,

66

'Ah, Tallmadge wants us to think nothing important would be sent out so openly, but we're not that stupid.' Someone warned the head of the party which greeted you in the ravine." He laid a hand on Grant's shoulder. "I hated doing this the way I had to. But I'd do it again, if it were the only way. Believe me, my choice of you was no slur on your intelligence or your loyalty. Rather, it's a tribute to your determination."

"Suppose Clinton smells a rat?" asked Grant.

"I don't think he will," answered Tallmadge. "The bulk of our army will move as though the orders were genuine. He'll think we're ready to strike down onto Manhattan. What we'll see later on the north shore of Long Island will tell us if our plan has worked. Now let's get back to the inn."

"There's something that's been bothering me. I've got it now," said Grant thoughtfully.

"Got what?"

"Really, it's nothing more than an impression. But I think I heard a woman's voice back there in the ravine."

"A woman?" cried Tallmadge, looking sharply at him.

"Yes," said Grant stubbornly, "I think so."

"Jim Thatcher, the surgeon, told me that women ride with the gangs in Westchester, but not here." They were nearing the inn. Tallmadge raised his voice a little, and spoke as though continuing a conversation. "And maybe after all it was my fault. I should have sent a strong escort out tonight with you."

"Might have helped," said Grant in the same tone. Then in a lower pitch he said, "There *was* a woman in that ravine."

Two days later Grant stood on the porch of the inn. A swift thunderstorm had finally drifted off down the Sound in thinning banks of black clouds. He looked anxiously, fearfully, toward the shore for any sign that Clinton's flotilla might be massing for that attack on the French at Newport. The packet taken from him in the ravine might have scotched those British plans, but he

67

couldn't be sure. Sundown could see the Sound thick with sails.

He sat just out of reach of the eaves that still dripped and gurgled. The sky above was a clean-swept blue and the great elms sparkled to the sun, their leaves rustling under a brisk wind. The town was coming to life after the brief battering of the storm. Small boys were resuming their endless games in ruined houses. Across Ash Creek a line of oxcarts headed for the bridge. A man rode past them, heading for the inn at a gallop. As he drew closer Grant recognized Caleb Brewster wrapped in a huge damp-looking boat-cape. He pulled up by the inn and swung clear of the saddle with an agility amazing for a man his size, and a seaman as well.

"Hello!" he cried, "The major tells me you're a captain now."

"Yes," said Grant. He looked at Brewster's right hand swathed in red-splotched bandages. "Any news from the Sound?" he asked quickly.

"Some. Where's the major?"

"Not here," answered Grant. "Be back by sundown."

Brewster wiped his forehead. "I wish he wouldn't stay close to the shore so much. Last year at Black Rock they took General Silliman and his son right out of their beds. Things wouldn't run so smooth if they took the major. Looks funny now out there on the Sound. Lots of light craft coming out from Long Island. Last night I had a quarrel with some English individuals. Two of my boats against two whaleboats and a snow." He held up his injured hand.

"Were they just patrolling?"

"That, with maybe a touch of the corduroy trade — some call it the London trade. I call it just plain smuggling. Tory craft met some of our people who don't mind trading with the enemy, in mid-Sound. Well, the snow and the whaleboats are berthed over in Black Rock now." He squinted toward the distant bridge. "There's part of their cargo now."

Grant followed his gaze and could just make out a group of men with high cocked hats. "Hessians!" he exclaimed.

Brewster nodded. "Sailing under a Tory skipper. He was supposed to take them on to Oyster Bay, but I persuaded him to change his sailing orders. Rest of the cargo was good, too. It'll be sold for the benefit of the state. Look at this." He brought out a thick package from his bags, stripped off the paper and held out some brown, ribbed cloth. "Better take this bolt. You could make a nice pair of breeches out of it." He thrust the bundle into Grant's hands.

Grant was about to protest when he felt paper crackle deep within the folds of cloth. "Thanks," he said quickly. "I certainly can use this."

Brewster winked. "I thought you'd know what to do with it. By the way, a man asked about you not far from here. Said you had the primest pair of rifled pistols he'd ever seen."

Through the peace of the sunlit afternoon, the other side of the Sound seemed suddenly close to Grant. So once more Austin Roe had journeyed from Culper's rooms to the creeks along Setauket Bay. He returned Brewster's gaze. "If you see him again, tell him that the pistols and I are thriving."

"He'll be glad to know." Brewster thrust a foot awkwardly into the stirrup.

"What's your hurry?" asked Grant. "Come in and try some of Mr. Nangle's West India rum."

"Like to," said Brewster, mounting deftly, "but I have to get back to Black Rock and see that the militia guard doesn't let those Hessians wander into wrong pastures." He waved his bandaged hand. "My duty to the major."

When Brewster had ridden off, Grant took the corduroy bundle up to his room. Carefully he spread the cloth out on his narrow bed, fold by fold, smoothing the surface with his palm lest some bit of fragile paper be torn. At length he saw a thick letter appear, addressed in a familiar hand, to John Bolton, Esq., care of Abraham Woodhull in Setauket. Quickly he covered it with his hand, drew it carefully to him and slid it into his pocket. Grant patted the rest of the cloth appreciatively. As he shook out the remaining folds, two official-looking sheets fastened together at one corner tumbled out. On the reverse side in clumsy script was written: Taken by me, Caleb Brewster, (Captain, Continental Artillery) from the cabin of the British snow *Dancer*.

Grant sat down on the bed and read the sheets. They contained a long list of instructions concerning a series of beacons that ran from the Morris House on the cliffs above Harlem River to Setauket and beyond. The sites were named precisely. One at Norwich Hill south of Oyster Bay, Sutton Hill by Cow Neck Point, Flushing Heights near Ustic's house, the high ground "Near to the house of Abraham Woodhull." One fire was to be lit at each spot under certain conditions, two under another and so on. All these signals were to be most carefully observed by any of His Majesty's ships in the East River or the Sound, said the order, and such ships were to answer by smokepot, by colors or by false fires. And the meaning of each signal and each answer was set down clearly.

He folded the sheets carefully. Tallmadge had said that what they saw on the north shore of Long Island would tell them if the Commander's ruse had worked. Now, with Brewster's discovery, they certainly could read smoke by day and fire by night, and they could be sure.

With Culper's letter and the British orders in his pocket, Grant left the inn. He struck out over Mill Plain toward Greenfield Hill with its fine view of the Sound. As he jumped the boggy banks of Mill Brook, he heard a rattle behind him and saw a light, open carriage weaving south. In it he made out two bonnets and a cocked hat. He ran toward the carriage, Greenfield Hill forgotten.

As Grant dropped from the bank onto the road, Laurel cried out, "Oh, it's Mr. Ledyard. Do stop!"

The carriage came to a grudging halt and Grant whipped off his hat, bowing. "I'd been hoping for a chance to ride over and pay my respects," he said.

Laurel smiled in acknowledgment of his greeting. Beside her, Mrs. Delmar put in briskly, "We're nearly settled now, Mr. Ledyard. We'd be glad to welcome you." From the other seat, Jethro Hollis touched his sober hat. "Yes, indeed. When I saw you the other day, I hadn't realized that you'd looked after my young ladies clear across Long Island. The family is much in your debt. I'd be glad to hear your impressions of the Island. It's been a closed land to us for so long."

"I'll be glad to. Perhaps when I call — "

"Why not join us now?" said Mrs. Delmar. "Unless of course you are pressed."

"I was only out for a walk," answered Grant.

"Then do ride with us," urged Laurel. "We're going into Black Rock."

"By all means," echoed Mr. Hollis heartily. "I've got to appraise officially some seized smuggled goods, and you can squire the ladies while I'm busy."

Grant climbed in and the carriage rolled on. Facing Laurel as he was, it was hard to divide his attention between her and the two elders. She seemed completely changed, as though a cloud had lifted from her. The weariness and discouragement that sometimes showed in her voice was gone, and her eyes danced with a quiet happiness. Grant heard about the settling in the little house above the river, of the white kitten she had found in her room, of the spinnet that had such a perfect tone. All was well along the Aspetuck, Mr. Hollis assured him. He was sorry Rosa was not with them, but she had flown off over the hills that morning on her horse, "like a tanager" Mr. Hollis said.

The carriage rolled onto the long spur formed by Ash Creek and the harbor. Disaster had not touched the little town of Black Rock. There the homes of the Wheelers and the Bartrams, the Sillimans and Pennfields stood serene in the sun. Mr. Hollis called to the driver to pull up by a wharf where a big warehouse loomed.

"Be here twenty minutes to a half hour," he rumbled. "There's a pretty walk down to the shore."

Mrs. Delmar cocked her head. "What's the contraband?"

"All sorts of things, Ann. Cloth, salt, wine, coffee, tea, I suppose."

"H'm," said Mrs. Delmar briskly. "And it'll be put up at auction later, of course. Jethro! Do you think I'm ninny enough to stew in the sun when I could be poking through bales and boxes?" She turned to Grant and Laurel. "If you young people want to skitter about and get sand in your shoes, you're welcome to. I'm going into the warehouse."

Grant hesitantly said to Laurel, "Shall we walk down the shore?"

"I'd like it," she replied.

The sun was still high, but the low ridge that ran down the Black Rock spur cut off some of the rays and a cool land breeze flooded from the north. Laurel slipped off her bonnet and dangled it by its green strings. "It's nice here!" she sighed, tilting her head to catch the low rustle and gurgle of the tide under the wharves. "I hope that you didn't really want to explore the warehouse." He shook his head, admiring the proud lift to her chin and the silken sheen of her blonde hair. "So you're going to begin a new life here," she went on.

The words were casual enough, but there was in her tone a hint of friendly acceptance of him as a person, not merely as a chance-met stranger in odd times. He felt a sudden impulse to tell her of his taking up service again, but the recollection of Tallmadge's approval of his silence concerning his status checked him. Looking at her out of the corner of his eye he answered thoughtfully, "That may be. I've got to start somewhere."

Laurel smiled at him. "I do hope it'll be here. We'd all be glad. You must talk to Uncle Jethro. He knows so many people. You're new to this part of the country, aren't you?"

"Yes. I'm from Massachusetts," he answered. It was good to stroll in the sun like this, with everything heightened by Laurel's obvious interest in him. It was good, too, to see her walking daintily along beside him, her face turning to him every now and then, and the wide sweep of her skirts rustling in the light breeze. He'd have been proud to escort her across the Yard at a Harvard commencement, or under the elms that fringed the Common at Worcester.

"And you don't want to go back there?" asked Laurel.

"To Worcester? In some ways, yes. It's a nice town and my family's always lived there. My father and I — my mother died when I was quite young — were always very close. I was due to graduate from Harvard with the class of '78 and then we were going to set up in law together. Ledyard and Ledyard. I always liked the sound of that."

"But it wasn't possible in these times," he went on, clinging to the idea of an entirely civilian background. "But maybe I'll go back there. It's so hard to get word through these days. I've not heard from Father in over a year." He gave a short laugh. "Perhaps it'll take another year to get a letter from here to Worcester. In the meantime, Fairfield is going to grow again. Perhaps Father will come down and join me here. There might be opportunities." He smiled inwardly. Part of what he said was true. More than a year had gone by since he had heard from his father in far-off Worcester, and there was no telling how long it would take a letter to get there now. Also, there were opportunities in Fairfield, but scarcely the sort to interest a lawyer.

At the foot of Grover's Hill at the far end of the point, they turned and started back toward the warehouses, Laurel asking about the study of law and if Grant didn't think he might be able to continue his work in Fairfield. "Uncle Jethro will help, I know," she concluded.

At the front of the warehouse they saw Mrs. Delmar sitting on a bench looking out over the harbor. "Was there anything interesting, Aunt Ann?" called Laurel.

"Interesting?" Mrs. Delmar flounced her bonnet energetically. "Stuff! There is a bolt or two of corduroy that I'm going to ask

Jethro to bid on, though. It'd make a nice habit for you, my dear."

"I'm sorry you were disappointed, Mrs. Delmar," Grant said. "I hope you had better luck, sir," he added as Mr. Hollis appeared in the wide doorway.

Mr. Hollis rubbed his blunt chin. "Maybe I'll try to pre-empt. Save money in the long run. The army's bad off for clothes." He went on in a maze of technical details concerning Connecticut bills, requisitions and the nearly empty national treasury. Jethro Hollis had a trick of sniffing in the midst of a sentence, of flicking a fingernail sharply against one of his sober coat buttons to emphasize a point.

When his exposition was ended, Laurel said quickly, "Uncle Jethro, Mr. Ledyard tells me he may settle around here somewhere. Couldn't you advise him?"

Mr. Hollis turned his sharp eyes on Grant appraisingly. "Yes. Be glad to. I've been hoping for a talk with Mr. Ledyard. I'd like to know his views on a good many points." He pulled out a sullen-faced watch. "Now, my ladies, if you're quite ready —"

All three turned and stared toward the Sound as a flat muffled report came from the hidden battery on the other side of Grover's Hill. Mrs. Delmar exclaimed, "What's that nonsense?"

Laurel, color fading, stepped closer to Grant, her eyes on him. He smiled reassuringly. "Nothing to be alarmed about. Probably just a practice shot." He tried to appear confident as he looked south. The bulge of Grover's Hill hid quite a stretch of water from him and the expanse to right and left seemed empty. Then beyond the east shoulder of the hill, a fine line showed, a thin, slanting hairline that moved slowly. It grew, swelled, became a bowsprit, the forward part of a hull, a whole two-masted vessel with the British colors at the peak. The little guns at the fort slapped the air again with their feeble reports, but the ship, well out of range, slid on along the blue line of the Sound.

Mr. Hollis sniffed. "Nothing. Happens all the time. Our boys are wasting their powder. The ship'll come about and head west

74

when it reaches Pennfield Reef out there. Come along, we're wasting daylight."

Laurel still stood looking seaward. Mrs. Delmar caught Grant's eye and raised an admonitory finger. Grant, hoping he had interpreted her signal correctly, said, "Would it inconvenience you if I rode with you, at least as far as Greenfield Hill?"

Mrs. Delmar looked secretly pleased and Laurel, facing Grant, said quickly, "We'd be so glad to have you, Mr. Ledyard."

The carriage rolled out of town and across the flats. Laurel talked on. She was anxious for winter, she said. She wanted to see a blizzard driving over the ridge, bringing the clean, bare smell of snow and icy winds. Grant, his back to the horses, put in a word from time to time. When the crest of the shoulder was reached, he made his adieus. He was in their debt for a most pleasant afternoon. Of course he would call. Friday? To be sure.

Alone on the shoulder, Grant turned as though to make his way to the observation post. Then he stopped. A wide stretch of the western Sound was before him, thick with sail. In the van, bearing on in the wake of that first vessel that had drawn fire from the fort were fast, lightly-armed craft, canvas golden against the deepening blue. After them lumbered wide-hulled ships, their decks bright with uniforms. One, five, seven transports, flanked by ships of the line. They were bearing east toward Newport in heavy menace. Sometime during the night, the leaders would raise the east tip of Long Island where they would meet the real striking force of the Royal Navy. The Commander's desperate ruse must have failed.

Grant started down the hill toward Fairfield. As he neared the inn he saw Benjamin Tallmadge riding up, his head back and plume floating defiantly from the crest of his helmet. Grant cried out in greeting and reached the steps of the Oxbow just as the major drew rein. There was something so reassuring in the lift of Tallmadge's head, in his poise, that Grant felt his own sense of helpless futility ebbing.

75

Grant called, "You've seen what's out there in the Sound?"

"Yes," said Tallmadge, dismounting. "Let's go up to my room." Upstairs, Tallmadge threw open a window looking out to the bright spatter of sail on the waters. "So Clinton was not taken in," observed Grant somberly.

"Either that, or none of the orders have reached him," answered Tallmadge. Then he smiled at Grant. "Keep your chin up. We've done what we could."

"And it wasn't enough."

"How do we know? A storm may yet scatter the whole flotilla. A fresh French fleet may be tacking into Newport at this minute." He tossed off his helmet and sat down by the window. "Perhaps I'm too hopeful." He turned to face Grant. "Let's look at things coolly. Suppose this force does get to Newport and crush Rochambeau. Take yourself as an individual American soldier. What do you say we do then?"

"Do?" Grant hesitated. "Why — I'd say — No, by God, I know! There's only one thing. That's to keep on doing what we can with what we have."

Tallmadge's chin went up. "That is the answer I needed." He rose and strode to the table, saber clanking. "Damn it, that's what ninety per cent of the country'd say. Now Lincoln lost a whole army there at Charleston, as I hardly need remind you. Have we given up the Southern states? No. Damned if we have. A new force is going overland into the Carolinas under Gates. He hasn't got much, but he'll do what he can with what he has."

Grant picked up a quill pen and twirled it between his fingers. "Yes," he said, "what would any sane man have bet on our chance after we got kicked out of Long Island and Manhattan? Or when we were at Valley Forge?"

"I'll tell you something else," said Tallmadge. "The Commander is playing his present gamble to the limit. Today I met Alec Hamilton. The whole army's on the move. We've drawn men from the camps at Preakness, at Kakiat and Paramus. Our big strength is east of the Hudson and orders still hold for a stroke at Manhattan by Kingsbridge."

"That's good," said Grant. "But can we handle Manhattan?"

Tallmadge raised his eyebrows tolerantly. "Have we ever had enough troops to handle anything? Of course, we know how many men Clinton's sending east, thanks to Culper."

"Culper!" shouted Grant. "Oh, my God. I ought to be reduced to the infantry." Belatedly he pulled out the papers Brewster had given him.

At once the major went to work with his chemicals. "H'm," he observed, "he's warning us. Something's brewing and so far he hasn't been able to get onto the trail. It's — eh! What's this?" He laid down the sheet, drumming with his long fingers on the table. "Look here, Ledyard, in coming across Long Island, did you by any chance hear the name John Anderson?"

"John Anderson? No."

"It's got something to do with this scare of Culper's but whether in a beneficent or maleficent way he can't say. Keep it in mind. John Anderson." He reached for the other papers. "What's all this?"

"Something Caleb picked out of a snow that he surged athwart, to use his own expression. A British signal code. I'd say it was worth a lot."

Tallmadge nodded. "These things are helpful."

Together they studied the sheets, marking off on a map the spots where the Manhattan and Long Island beacons were located. At last the major rolled up the map. "This will go to the Commander. We'll make a copy of it later tonight and send a trooper on with it."

Grant turned toward the window. Light was fading. He started when Tallmadge spoke briskly. "Let's have a bite of supper under Mr. Moobie's antic eye and then a good walk for digestion's sake."

"A walk?"

"Why not? A view of the Sound from the top of Greenfield Hill."

When the two reached the crest, a light veil of clouds drifted over the summer stars. In the Sound, the lights of the British ships glowed as the flotilla beat its stubborn way east toward Newport and the French. Tallmadge drew out a small spyglass and squinted through it. Grant stretched flat on the ground, lining up one particularly bright green light against a low bush ahead of him. The green glimmer seemed stationary, but as he watched, it vanished behind the bush, then appeared on the other side of it. He lifted himself on his elbow and held up a moistened finger that grew suddenly cool. An invisible current of air was flowing over the hills, catching the sails in the very quarter for which every sailing master down there was undoubtedly praying. "Blast them!" he growled. "They're moving, Major."

"Bad," said Tallmadge tersely. "We've got nothing afloat to stop them with, and they'll keep out of range of anything we've got on shore."

"Maybe the breeze will die," began Grant hopefully. Then he swore under his breath. "Die be damned! It's freshening. Look. The clouds are lifting. There's a star — another — low on the horizon. Another — ." Then with a muffled shout he sprang to his feet, caught Tallmadge by the shoulder. "The signals! The signal code that Caleb captured. Those aren't stars. By God, they're beacons! There's one by Flushing. Look. The nearest glow! That must be Woodhull's and there's another, farther east!"

Tallmadge said calmly, "I believe you're right, Grant."

Grant shouted again. "The ships! They're answering!"

As he spoke, a rocket twisted red, high in the air, flowered in a shower of sparks. Glowing clusters rose slowly as signal lights were hoisted on a dozen masts. Then the Sound was dark, save for the port and starboard lanterns on the hidden ships.

Grant's hands trembled. "West! They're all turning west. God

78

above, they're going home! They've been recalled. Newport's safe!"

To his surprise he found that the imperturbable Tallmadge was trembling, too. There was a moment's pause. Then the major said quietly, "Yes. The Commander will be pleased."

Tallmadge drew a long breath. "You know, I think that Mr. Nangle would like to see us in the taproom."

Grant and Tallmadge went side by side down the hill path. Below them, far out in the Sound, the long procession of lights beat slowly west into the wind. Rochambeau and his French troops could land safely. Tallmadge said gravely, "Some one of those orders must have reached Clinton and frightened him enough to cancel the whole movement. Perhaps the papers he saw were the ones you carried."

"What of it?" said Grant quickly. "The important thing is that one set got to him." He laughed. "God, I'd have looked silly, yelling and stamping up there, if the signals had only meant to send a long boat to Flushing to pick up some fat colonel."

Tallmadge shook his head. "They *had* to mean what they did. And what they really meant was that we'll have thousands of trained, equipped Frenchmen marching with us."

V

Laurel Dane

In the hot, weary days that followed, Sir Henry Clinton's British and Hessians, duped by the Commander's feigned attack on Manhattan, tramped ashore from their transports. The American Army quietly melted away on the east bank of the Hudson, its thin regiments filing off to their base camps. A deep quiet hung over the Sound as the surf hissed softly on the sands of the Fairfield beaches.

On high Redding Ridge, fifteen miles inland, Grant sat his mare and watched the afternoon sun strike the shaggy crests to the east, while the western slopes showed patches of purpling shadow. On a mission for Tallmadge, he had spent the last two days scouting the country clear from the Poquonock, across the upper waters of Mill River and the Tatetuck and down the Aspetuck that flowed below him in the darkening valley. As he shifted in the saddle, paper crackled in an inner pocket and he cursed it. If only Tallmadge had met him last night as planned, the whole troublesome business would be off his hands.

He turned the mare and cantered north along the ridge to the house of old Mr. Sammis, where Tallmadge was to meet him. As he reached the long, low porch of the Sammis house, he rose in his stirrups, hoping for a glimpse of the major. But Mr. Sammis sat there alone, a stick between his knees. Grant dismounted, gave his mare to a stable boy and came wearily up the side steps. "Any news of the major, Mr. Sammis?" he asked.

"Not a sign," said the old man, shaking his thin, white hair. He pushed up a low chair. "Sit by, sit by. I've been lonely today."

Grant settled himself to listen resignedly to Mr. Sammis's interminable tales of the old French wars.

Mr. Sammis gave a reedy chuckle. "It came to me this morning that I'd forgotten one mighty important thing about that time we hit Baron Dieskau. When I was telling you about it last night, I forgot there was — reckon there is to this very day — an old trail that runs south from Lake George and I had my company — "

Grant's face set in a frozen smile and he managed a nod from time to time, his thoughts on the troublesome letter in his pocket. That letter had arrived last night, carried by a trooper who had orders to wait for an answer and who was probably lounging around the stables at that very moment. It was addressed to Tallmadge and marked *"Urgent!"* Tallmadge had given Grant unequivocal orders to act for him in all matters while he was away. The paper crackled again as Grant shifted in his chair.

Old Mr. Sammis talked on. Eyes half closed, Grant could see before him the words on the paper: " . . . my wish to further all possible work that may be carried out from this post . . . utmost importance to our country that I know what transpires among our enemies in New York City . . . request that you furnish me at once with the names and whereabouts of reliable patriots engaged in confidential work or who may wish to undertake such work." The last paragraph expressed much esteem for Tallmadge. Below was the bold, unmistakable signature, "B. Arnold, Maj. Gen'l."

There was no questioning the validity of Benedict Arnold's request. As chief of the vital West Point area, intelligence would be one of his most important duties. Grant knew enough of the workings of the New York-Setauket-Fairfield Headquarters channel to write out a valuable summary for Arnold. Mr. Sammis droned on, but Grant rose suddenly, and broke in, "Mr. Sammis, may I trouble you for writing materials?"

"Eh?" Mr. Sammis looked annoyed. "Why, I hadn't more than begun about — "

Grant flushed. "It was thoughtless of me to interrupt, sir. But this is a matter of duty."

"Duty? By crimus, I know a soldier's duty as well as the next man. This way, Mr. Ledyard."

The room on the first floor looked north over the rolling meadows, now touched with the last rays of day. Grant pulled up to a low mahogany escritoire, squared his elbows and dipped his quill in the silver inkpot. He hesitated, pushed back and began to pace up and down the room, fussing with a book, studying the wallpaper. He sat down, got up again. The room grew dimmer and dimmer. "God damn it," he fumed. "What's the matter with me?" He paced on. Why should he hold back? Was it the memory of the long court-martial of Arnold the year before, the heavy charges brought against him? Hardly. Those charges had involved, at worst, slackness in administration, an inability to account for funds entrusted to him or funds that had accrued to him in the past. Grant dismissed the idea. Like most combat soldiers, he had an ingrained distrust of the business end of the army, of the desk-soldiers who were unable to understand that, in the swift moving course of a campaign, an officer could not be as particular about vouchers and receipts as a clerk back of a counter.

He went out to the kitchen where a silent, angular woman gave him bread and cold beef and coffee. Through the window that looked out to the stables, he saw the trooper who had brought the letter smoking his pipe, waiting for the answer.

Briskly he strode back to the little room, lit the candles on the escritoire and began to write. "In the absence of Major Benjamin Tallmadge, I have the honor to comply with the — " He threw down his pen, crumbled the sheet. He was on his feet again, pacing, turning, pacing, unconsciously moving farther and farther from his chair.

As he stood by the door, he caught the sound of many hoofs. He ran out onto the porch as a clear voice cried, "Ah, Benoni! See to my horse and there's a sixpence for you. Mr. Ledyard here?"

Tallmadge was coming toward him while four troopers were busy with their own mounts and a pair of pack horses. Grant cried, "Anything serious delay you, Major?"

Tallmadge, shook his head, smiling. "You've a report for me?" he asked.

"I've covered the ground you assigned me. It's no good for your chain of posts."

"Why not?"

"Steep hills. Deep valleys. They'd double your distance and treble your time in getting from post to post."

Tallmadge gave a satisfied nod and his white plume swished about his shoulders. "That's what I wanted to know. We'll stick to the shore. Who's that trooper? A message? You've handled it, I suppose."

"No," answered Grant slowly. "Perhaps I should have. I don't know."

"You had authority, you know."

"In this case, I'm not sure."

Grant led the way into the candlelit room, placed a chair for Tallmadge by the escritoire and handed him Arnold's letter.

The major opened the letter as he seated himself. Grant watched him uneasily. "This came last night?" Tallmadge asked quietly. "And you've done nothing about it?"

"Nothing."

Tallmadge's eyes were on the word "Urgent" but he made no comment as he turned to the body of the letter. The room was still. Outside, Grant heard crickets shrilling in the long meadow grass and a cow lowing uneasily from the stables.

When Tallmadge had finished reading, he sat motionless. Then he spoke, slowly and carefully, "Grant, I'm afraid that the Commander won't like this. Arnold's request is perfectly reasonable and I assume he's making it to every one in touch with work like this. Why did you delay?"

"Damn it," said Grant. "I held off as long as I could, hoping you'd be here. I tried to draft a reply tonight, and I tell you I *couldn't*. I just couldn't put down on paper all that I know about our friends to the south."

"I never thought you'd be afraid of responsibility, Grant," observed Tallmadge.

"To hell with the responsibility. I wasn't afraid of that. I was afraid for *them*."

"Arnold will be furious," said Tallmadge.

"That can't be helped. If I was wrong, I was wrong."

Tallmadge thought for a moment. Then he said quickly. "No. You were right, though I don't know quite *why*. I'll draft a reply that may soothe Arnold, and I'll have a talk with the Commander." His face grew dark. "We've got to be careful with everything and everybody. I've just found out that there's a bad leak to the British. It's been going on for months and it runs through Fairfield County into Westchester. Now come up to the room that Mr. Sammis has been saving for me, and let's see what the troopers have been dragging up the stairs."

They found Mr. Sammis holding a candle for them at the head of the narrow, twisting stairs. "Waiting for you, Major," he cried. "Bed turned down, candles lit." He showed them into a clean, cool chamber where white curtains fluttered gently at the windows. Tallmadge stepped over to a neat stack of boxes and bundles and carefully unknotted their cords. "Here's the first item."

Grant gave a whistle of admiration. A silver-gray cavalry jacket lay inside. The sky-blue of its high, rolled collar was repeated in the facings and lining and in the deep, turned-back cuffs.

"Hi-yi," chuckled Mr. Sammis. "Fit for Mars himself."

"And look at these breeches. White leather — soft as silk and tough as hickory. Here are dragoon boots with a flap to protect the tendons above the knees. Grant, do you mind opening that wooden case?"

The helmet that lay inside gleamed like silver. From its high, curved crest trailed a long, silky plume of white hair and a band

84

of leopard skin circled the space just above the visor. The chin strap was of finely-worked metal scales.

"Like 'em?" asked Tallmadge when the whole array was spread out on the bed.

Grant nodded enviously, while Mr. Sammis quavered, "Jehoshaphat!"

"Now, Grant, do you think you can take a little better care of these than you did of the clothes that I've seen you in?" Tallmadge smiled at him.

"My God! Do you mean those are mine?" exclaimed Grant.

"Of course they're yours. Not exactly regulation, but we wear what we can get."

Grant riffled his fingers through the trailing plume of the helmet, felt of the fine weave of the jacket. "It's better than I've ever owned. What is it? Captured stuff?"

"French," said Tallmadge, indicating the careful stitching about the button holes. "Last year, Lafayette fitted out the whole Light-Infantry Corps from his own pocket and threw in a few cavalry rigs to boot. This is one of them. You'll find his monogram on the saber in the case there."

The fit was surprisingly good, even to the sleeves of the long waistcoat that matched the sky-blue collar and facings of the jacket. Grant tramped happily up and down the room, making quick lunges with the well-balanced saber.

"I haven't felt this way since my father bought me my first grown-up clothes and took me down to swim in Quinsigamond," said Grant happily.

Mr. Sammis eyed him solemnly. "It's fitting for a soldier to take pride in his uniform."

When the old man had gone, Grant asked, "What's our next task?"

"Setting up our coastal posts. We'll use the same sites that we talked about in Fairfield. New London, Lyme, Guilford, New Haven, Stratford, Green Farms, and Stamford. Three troopers to

85

a post to act as watchers and couriers. What I want you to do is to go back to Fairfield tomorrow and see what Caleb Brewster may have brought in. I'll join you there the day after."

"I see," said Grant. "Ah — by the way — have you any objection to my going down the Aspetuck?"

Tallmadge grinned. "By all means. My respects to Jethro Hollis, and any others you may chance to meet there. I thought you told me, though, that the young lady isn't partial to uniforms."

"That's so. But I think this may be different."

"Does she seem afraid?"

"No," answered Grant. "Not afraid at all. It's sort of a revulsion, I'd say, a freezing up."

"Interesting," said Tallmadge. "Well, start when you please tomorrow. Keep your eyes and ears open." He unfastened his high, black stock. "You remember my asking you once if you'd ever heard the name John Anderson?"

"Yes, very well."

"You've still not come across it?"

Grant shook his head. "No. What's it all about? Do you think it has anything to do with the leak you spoke of?"

"Oh no," answered Tallmadge. "This Anderson business is something new. Your room's just across the hall, isn't it? I'll call you when I get up and we'll have coffee together before you start."

The early morning sky was cloudless. A brisk autumn wind rippled down the valley of the Aspetuck as Grant followed it south. He whistled, happy to be in uniform again. His fine cloak, whose colors reversed those of his uniform, was neatly rolled on the pommel in a waterproof case, and the new leather saddlebags were chased with the Marquis's monogram.

The sun was topping the eastern crest, flooding in rich glow over the level meadows. People were moving about in the fields. He found himself swinging his head to the rhythm of the hoofs while doggerel lines formed in his mind:

86

From the Naugatuck to the Tatetuck,
And the Saugatuck to the Aspetuck!

The miles slid easily by under the climbing sun, and at last he recognized the hill which must hide Jethro Hollis's house. As he mounted the long ascent between towering oaks, he bent from the saddle, frowning. It was clear that not long before sunrise, several riders had passed that way. The hoof marks were sharp and well defined and had been made when the surface was still wet with dew. Although raids and forays were common enough in Westchester County, the Aspetuck Valley and the country to the east were relatively peaceful. If not a patrol, who could have ridden that way? As he settled himself in the saddle, Grant recalled his first visit. Several men had ridden off as he and the ladies arrived. Probably they, like these riders, were solid citizens of the district who had come to consult with Hollis as a member of the assembly. But the early hour of this last visit seemed odd. Was there some emergency?

Grant pushed the black into a lively trot. The gravel of the drive crunched under the black hoofs as he pulled up by the porch of the Hollis house, hand raised to his helmet. Jethro Hollis stared at him in surprise from a chair by the door. "My duty to you, Mr. Hollis," Grant called.

The older man was on his feet at once, beaming a welcome. "Bless my soul! The ladies' escort! So you've taken the right path, have you? A captain, no less. I wondered when I first saw you if you were one of those people who let someone else fight our war."

Grant smiled. "Sometimes circumstances keep you high and dry on the bank. I plunged in as soon as I could."

Hollis came down the steps and stood stroking the black's glossy neck. "H'm. I see. Or do I? It seems to me the ladies said you brought them clear across Long Island."

"That's correct," answered Grant. "The British pulled me out of the river of war. I finally managed to get away from them."

Still stroking the black, Hollis said, "That must have been difficult."

"I was lucky. They were bringing me up from the South."

Hollis gave him a keen glance. "So you were taken with Lincoln and his men. And you've had a look at New York. You must have had some interesting things to tell our military."

Grant replied indifferently, "Little enough. Things happened so fast that I was clear before I really knew it."

"Of course," said Hollis thoughtfully. "But I'll be glad, Captain Ledyard, if you'd spare me an evening to tell me what you saw and heard — in detail. In fact, in my capacity as member of the Assembly, it's really my duty to question you."

"Civilian over military?" laughed Grant. "You appoint a time, Mr. Hollis."

Hollis nodded in satisfaction. "I'll write you. In the meantime, I've hardly given you a chance to inquire about the ladies, but I may say that they flourish. Laurel was here not fifteen minutes ago with Mrs. Delmar. You'll find them at the upper house." He raised his hand in farewell and went back to the porch.

Grant rode up to the Delmar house. He rapped lightly on the solid green door with the hilt of his saber.

From the left end of the porch he heard a stifled cry, "Grant!" Laurel was looking at him, lips slightly parted. Delighted by her sudden appearance and by her use of his Christian name, he whipped off his helmet. "I was just riding by and — "

"You've become a soldier," she said in a stifled tone.

"No. Re-become, if you like. They've made a captain out of me. Tell me about yourself now. How have — what's the matter?" He broke off.

She said, "A soldier. I thought — "

Grant gave an indignant laugh. "What else would you expect in these times?"

"You didn't tell me — tell us, I mean. You made us all think that you weren't a killer, that you were going to settle down in Fairfield."

"And so I may. Who knows? Here, let me pull up this chair for you."

"No. Please, Mr. Ledyard. I must ask you to excuse me."

Grant's chin set stubbornly. "Without an explanation, Miss Dane?"

She looked straight at him. "Don't think I'm ungrateful. You did so much for us when we had no right to expect it of you. I remember Black Rock, too."

"I'm the same person who walked with you at Black Rock."

Her expression hardened. "I've got to say this. You think you're doing right. I don't. I never can."

Grant gave a wry smile. "Do you think that I commit treason by moving against the King?"

"No. But you are doing wrong. So is the King."

In spite of her words and her attitude, she seemed somehow more lovely and desirable than ever, standing there, slim in her blue gown, with her curls bright in the morning sun. He said gently, "You can't have realized what we've been through and what threatens us. Everything we believe in is in terrible danger. We have to fight. The same applies to most of the Tories I've known. They have to fight. They believe in the Crown. It all had to happen."

"It did *not!*" cried Laurel.

"Don't think any of us like to fight," he went on quickly. "But there comes a point when you have to — if your beliefs mean anything."

"No! No!" Her voice rose. "Nothing is worth this endless killing and killing and killing. You've all — all — become savages again like the Hurons and the Senecas and the Mohawks. At least, those poor Indians don't know any better. Some of you talk about liberty and some of you talk about the Crown. In the name of either you blast and hack at each other, burn homes, bring death to old people and children and sick people. You could have gotten this liberty in a dozen ways without murder, if what you wanted was right. And the Crown could have been supreme — if that had been the right way."

"Everything was tried, Miss Dane," said Grant.

"It couldn't have been — or you'd not be fighting now."

"You think, then, that there is never justification for killing?"

"Never."

"How about self-defense? Would you kill to save your own life?"

Her eyes wavered for a moment, then she said, "I hope I would be strong enough not to."

Grant went on. "You say we kill needlessly for an idea. I'd call it an ideal. Also, we offer ourselves to be killed for it."

She shook her head. "Before all this terrible business happened, you were intending for the law. Doesn't the law have a good deal to say against killing? But to you, the law seems to be something that can be set aside when it becomes inconvenient. Now really, I must ask you to excuse me." She stepped to the door, then turned to him, hand on the latch. "I — I could wish that you had stayed true to the law — that you were the same man I saw there at Onderdonk's." Then she was gone.

Frowning, Grant went down the steps, remounted and rode past the Hollis house and turned toward Fairfield. He still smarted from Laurel's dismissal of him — particularly in his new uniform. Just the same, she had not fled into the house at once, but had stayed to talk with him. And another thing — the very fact that she had seemed upset was a tacit admission of regard for him and concern about him, at least to some extent. She would have closed the door on a casual acquaintance. At the edge of the Hollis land, his horse tossed its head suddenly and he looked up to see Mrs. Delmar, very erect in brown sunbonnet and sensible brown dress, standing among some currant bushes, a basket over her arm. She bobbed her head at him. "I saw you ride in, but there was no chance to head you off," she began. "I'm very fond of Laurel."

"I can understand that," said Grant reining in.

"No doubt. Therefore, there are things that you ought to know. She saw a whole settlement wiped out. It wasn't a big slaughter like Cherry Valley, but it was very like it. Indians and Tories. Her brother led them on. Some people say that he killed her father. Laurel and some others got away somehow and then came back and tried to start life again. More people joined them and their chief idea seemed to be reprisal on the nearest Tory settlement. It was done most thoroughly. Then Laurel came here."

"I can see why wars and armies don't appeal to her," Grant said gravely.

The brown sunbonnet shook vigorously. "Her father and mother both felt that way about violence and so did she, she says, long before any of this happened. She believes war is evil. And don't think for an instant that it's timidity on her part. It's the sort of conviction that led people to the stake in the old days."

"I'm sure of that."

"What surprises me," went on Mrs. Delmar, "is that she didn't see the soldier under those rags you wore when we first saw you. You didn't astonish me one bit, riding in like a polished up Don Quixote." She sighed. "It's all a great pity. You had her confidence from the first. I'd have been glad for you to be her friend. It's too late now."

"You think so?"

"Yes," answered Mrs. Delmar simply.

Grant bowed. "Thank you for confiding in me."

"Stuff!" said Mrs. Delmar. "Well, get along with your trappings. I'll delay you no more. Just remember that your duty is to our thirteen states and not to the conversion of someone who can't be converted. God bless you."

Grant rode on, frowning. According to her, he would be well advised not to try to see Laurel again. He had felt a strong attraction for an unknown girl when she smiled at him at Onderdonk's. Chance had thrown her in his path at Black Rock. Now she dismissed him because he was a soldier. Why should he care? Resolutely he began to think of the chain of posts Tallmadge would establish along the coast, three troopers to a post. He tried to visualize the shore line as he had seen it on maps but his mind was illogically filled with the picture of Laurel, slimly rounded in her blue dress. The memory both warmed and exasperated him. She could be so appealing at one moment, and then suddenly turn so sharply critical, so ready to condemn utterly what he believed in. And yet, when she was most contrary, she was at her loveliest.

Off to the north he heard a faint drumming of hoofs. Across a long stretch of meadowland a girl rode at a gay gallop with her red hair streaming in the sun. Rosa Hollis! Grant checked his black for an instant, thinking that he might cut overland and meet her for at least a word. Then he saw a second rider, a tall, well-dressed man, whooping and laughing, pelting after her on a big roan. Grant kept on east and south.

In the days that followed, Grant was fully occupied in helping Tallmadge set up his chain of posts from New London to Stamford. The ranks of the 2nd had swelled during the summer. At first it had consisted mainly of Connecticut farmers, but now there were men of many trades, from New Hampshire, and even from Virginia.

Grant rode into the September sunrise that was glimmering over the rounded top of Compo Hill, following a twisting, sandy trail that led to the summit. The nodding grasses by the trailside and the short crisp turf beyond were rimmed with dew. Close to the crest, he halted to watch his five troopers ease their mounts up the slope. Two of them he would leave, with a sergeant, when he reached Green Farms a couple of miles beyond Compo. That post would complete Tallmadge's chain. The other two were to ride on with him to Fairfield.

He liked their looks, as they wound up toward him. Their equipment showed signs of hard wear but their arms were in excellent shape and the tears and rents in their uniforms were neatly mended. The rearmost trooper had been a watchmaker in New Jersey. Beyond him was a Rhode Island miller, shoulders always bent as though heaving a meal sack. Oddest of all was Sergeant Turner with his keen, sensitive face. In civil life he had been an itinerant portrait painter, roving the eastern seaboard from end to end. Somehow he had developed into an excellent cavalryman.

As the little command gained the top of the hill, Grant nodded to the sergeant, gathered his black and started on. He looked seaward but could make out only a golden dazzle touched with the faintest tinge of blue. Turner cantered up beside him. "Looks sort of funny, doesn't it?" observed the sergeant.

Grant's eyes followed his pointing hand and at last he saw what seemed an endless mass of floating mirrors. Then black spots danced about in a pattern.

"Make it out?" asked Turner.

"I'd give a hundred pounds of gold for your eyesight. Are those barges, whaleboats and a ketch lying off Sherwood Point?"

"Yes. The barges are beached and the whaleboats seem to be circling them; and they aren't ours. Trouble afoot, unless it's Clinton coming over to say the whole war's a mistake and he's very sorry."

Grant looked inland. Then he spun his black about. "Get off the skyline. Quick!" He started down the north slope, waving to the others to follow. In the shelter of a little pine grove, his men formed about him. He cocked his thumb at Turner. "Look across the salt pond, about northeast. See that round hill with the one dead tree against the sky?"

Turner's eyes narrowed. "I got it."

"Make it out, you others?" called Grant.

The hill beyond the dead tree was notched and through the notch straggled a road that must lead on down to the flats and Sherwood Point. There was color against the green of the notch and

93

the brown of the road, color and a steady winking of metal that edged a drab flow.

Trooper Murray, a wizened ex-flax teaser, rubbed his receding chin. "Cattle, folks. Looky, Cap — ain't much of a guard to them."

"How do you read it?" asked Turner quietly.

"A raid for cattle," said Grant. "They've got prisoners, too. Country people. There's not much of a guard and no cover party. Therefore," he wrinkled his forehead, "they knew no one would bother them on the raid. They knew just where to go and what to get."

"Meaning they were primed by someone on this side?" asked Turner.

"I'm afraid so. You've got a good eye for country. How far away are they?"

Turner stretched out his arm as though blessing the sun-touched land ahead of him. "Two miles. Maybe a little more."

The procession on the far hill was in full view now. Grant figured that a good fifty head of cattle were being driven to the waiting barges. Armed men he reckoned at twelve. He looked at his men. "Odds are a bit more than two to one. Now listen. There's a side valley west of that road. We'll hit up well beyond the rear of that column. Then, Turner, I want you to take the others and hit from the rear. Dead gallop and keep to the left. You'll have cover up until the last minute. Understand? Clean out the guards. As soon as you charge, I'll break out on the other side."

"Alone?"

Grant patted his holsters. "They'll think I'm a squadron. Now everyone got that clear? Surprise is the whole thing. If we aren't able to get it, we'll rally on the Fairfield road. There'll be no pursuit, I'm sure."

They crossed a salt marsh and wound into a sloping valley that roughly paralleled the march of the southbound raiders. Grant studied the terrain ahead intently, weighing distance, rate of progress and the twistings of the valley. A promontory of land rose before him, a path forking off along each flank. He pointed to the right fork.

Sergeant Turner, closing up from behind, said in a low voice. "Left, I think, sir."

"Sure?" asked Grant. Turner nodded emphatically. He seemed to know by instinct where a given brook would join a river, where two roads would meet or where rough ground would give way to smooth. "All right," Grant said, "left it is."

A few hundred yards on, Grant dropped to the ground and gave the signal to dismount, covering the last rod or so on foot. The road was empty of life, but its surface was thick with the marks of hoofs and boots. Grant raised his hand, then heard the soft creak of leather as his men mounted. "Take 'em sergeant," he muttered and stood for an instant watching them file quietly onto the road and head south in the wake of the raiders.

He mounted and rode among the trees on the right of the road. A confused murmur reached him, the shuffle of hoofs, the rustle of voices, an urgent shout or two. The raiders seemed in a hurry to reach their barges. He would strike a little ahead of mid-column while Turner and the others spread confusion from the rear.

The trees thinned. He found himself staring utterly unprepared at a thick column of oxen and a few men in nondescript uniforms. Instantly there was a crash and yell from the hidden rear. The man nearest him, face white under a battered Hessian helmet was struggling to unsling his musket. Then Grant caught the wink of the helmets of his own men. He charged down on the nearest section, firing carefully spaced shots. He had a confused vision of a squat man whirling toward him, musket across his chest. The man was gone, and the black cannoned off the shaggy side of an ox, skittered into a knot of men who were facing in all directions, yelling in wild confusion.

When the hammer of his pistol clicked on an empty pan, Grant drew his sword and raced to the head of the column roaring, "Mr. Mason! Bring on your troop. Bring it on, I say!" A man caught at his bridle and Grant knocked him down with the flat of his sword. Over a sea of tossing horses Grant could see Turner lunging at a man who fled up the west bank of the road. Another man broke away, then another, and the undergrowth crackled as the rest of the escort drove for safety. Two bodies lay still on the road.

Grant waved to Turner. "See to the rear of the column. Try and get the cattle headed back north." Then he felt a gentle tug at his stirrup and looked down with surprise. A wrinkled old woman gave him a curtsy. "Thank ye, sir. Thank ye!" she said.

Five or six other civilians crowded about him, old men and women. "Easy! Easy!" Grant said. "One at a time. How did it happen?"

No one could give him a clear account. Where the raiders had come from no one could say. At each house or farm there had been a sudden flare of torches and armed men pounding at the door. One man, younger than the others, had recognized one of the raiders. "Jamie Crothers it was who used to farm up Mud Brook way. He refugeed in '77 to Long Island."

"You're sure?" asked Grant.

"Sure positive. Got land now over west of Oyster Bay."

"Good," said Grant. "Report that and anything else you know to your Committee of Safety."

"Damn committees. Come the next fog, I'll raise fifty of the boys around here and we'll go over and see what *his* cattle are like."

Grant grinned at the broad, angry face. "That's the spirit." Then his grin faded. What good did it do? What would be gained by a new raid on Musketto Bay? Back and forth, looting and killing, from Connecticut to Long Island, from Long Island to Connecticut, an endless wheel of misery and suffering. He spoke crisply. "Anyway, you're safe now. Better get back to your homes. Take that lame man along with you for questioning by your committee."

The column began its slow movement north. Grant gathered his men about him. "That was very well done, all of you. Anyone hurt?"

Turner shook his head. "We hit 'em too quick and then they heard you on the other side. Who were you hollering to?"

"Just a name that came into my head," said Grant.

Turner gave a short laugh. "Sure did impress those Tories. When they get back to the barges, they'll tell of standing off a whole squadron."

Grant led the little group east across country. He had freed several citizens who would probably have been held for clandestine ransom on Long Island, as well as valuable cattle. He had not lost a man.

After Turner and two troopers were left at Green Farms, Grant rode back to Fairfield. He found Tallmadge's door open and he could see the major pushing away a vast pie and carefully cleaning a small knife and fork which he carried in a morocco case. "Detail completed," called Grant as he came in.

Tallmadge looked up with his pleasant smile. "Good enough, Grant. Strike any difficulties? Here, have some of this ambrosia pie."

"Thanks no," said Grant, seating himself. "Difficulties? Not a one. I started at New London, then came west. When I'd established the Stratford post, I hopped clear over to Stamford and then worked back to Green Farms and here."

Tallmadge picked up some papers from the table. "These your reports? I'll endorse them and send them on. Here! What's this? 'Ammunition expended.' I thought you didn't have any trouble."

Grant looked up. "Oh, that's separate. Hasn't anything to do with establishing the posts." He briefly outlined his brush with the raiders, the freeing of the prisoners and the cattle.

Tallmadge listened carefully. "Yes," he said finally, "I'm sure you're right. Whoever planned it on Long Island had news from here that the country would be safe. There's that leak I spoke of."

"But if someone in Connecticut sent word to Long Island, how did they happen to miss the fact that my group would be in that area?"

"Just reason it out, Grant. Someone knew that you had gone clear to New London and were working west from there," Tallmadge pointed out. "If you'd followed the logical course, you'd have been miles away from the scene of the raid. But instead, you made one long jump straight to Stamford and then doubled back, running into them as you did so. You say their surprise was complete?"

"Utterly, or we couldn't have handled them."

"That proves my point then. They'd been assured by someone they trusted, that they wouldn't run into anything more than a boy with a stick." Tallmadge returned to his papers. "This may interest you. The chain of posts is proving its worth already. Caleb Brewster ran into trouble coming back from Long Island last night. He put in at Stratford and there was one of your troopers ready to bring his messages here. Culper is still worried about John Anderson."

"Speaking of him," Grant put in, "did you hear anything more about Arnold's letter — you know, the one asking for lists of secret agents?"

"I have another letter from him. He was bland as molasses, hinting at promotion for me and repeating his request. Fortunately I've got permission to refer all such requests to the Commander. It's out of my hands." He got up, gathering his papers. "I'm off for Pound Ridge to see the colonel, thence to headquarters. I'll be gone two or three days."

Three days later Grant was sitting in Jethro Hollis's study. He had come to ask Hollis, as a member of the Assembly, to procure aid for those families who had been burned out by Tory raiders from across the Sound.

At the broad mahogany desk, Hollis settled back in his armchair and tapped the sheets Grant had brought him. "Very lucid, Ledyard, very. Does you credit. I can see why something like this might be necessary over in Westchester where times are violent. But I hardly see the need for it in Connecticut."

Grant studied him, somehow dissatisfied. While he could put his finger on no one point, it seemed to him that Hollis's interest was perfunctory, that he had been reading and listening with eyes and ears, not with his mind. He went on obstinately, "Just because the problem is smaller here doesn't mean that something shouldn't be done about it. If one farm is burned out and looted, that's just as important to the owners as though a dozen neighbors had suffered with them."

Hollis waved a stubby hand. "People can apply to the Assembly at Wethersfield for relief."

"But that doesn't help them," urged Grant. "They've got to have the essentials replaced quickly. In the Assembly, you haven't even decided if such claims will be granted, or when. I've read in the Hartford papers that they may have to wait till the end of hostilities."

"You, as a soldier," observed Hollis blandly, "surely know that the army faces even more uncertainty than the civilians. If the army can wait, certainly we can."

"No," said Grant quickly. "The civilians can't wait. Take the case of the Kents. They've a farm west of the Norwalk river. They were burned out and their cattle taken by a few boatloads from across the Sound. The Kents only had the clothes they stood in. My post in Stamford heard about them, drew on their own rations to feed them, lent them blankets and helped them rig up some sort of shelter. That's the second time the Kents have been raided and they were beginning to wonder if they could afford to stay patriots. Just that little help has saved them as good Americans, but my men can't do much of that. Their rations are slim enough and most units only have one blanket for every two men."

"Oh, I see your point, I see your point," said Hollis hurriedly. "The state of Connecticut, you feel, ought to maintain depots for the quick relief of such people. On paper, it's plausible, but we simply can't afford it."

"You can't afford not to. If people suffer too much without

relief, a lot of them are going to declare for the Crown just to live."

"You underestimate the staunchness of Connecticut people," said Hollis. "Besides, we'd be bankrupt in a month. I'll keep these notes of yours, but in your own interest I'd best not show them to other Assembly members. They'd resent being lessoned by a soldier, particularly one from another state. Oh, I meant to ask you if you'd shown this to Major Tallmadge."

"No. He only got back from headquarters yesterday and left at once for the Housatonic before I'd had more than a word with him. When he comes back — " He looked up impatiently at a rap from the door.

"Come in," called Hollis, obviously rather relieved.

Grant's eyes widened as Laurel appeared in the doorway. She was swathed from chin to ankles in a spotless blue apron. A rather severe mobcap covered her golden hair and a white dab of flour showed on her round chin. In her hands she held a big platter of freshly-made doughnuts, and the subtle fragrance flowed through the room. Grant was on his feet at once, bowing, while he wondered if Laurel had actually made the doughnuts herself. She certainly looked competent enough and domestic enough — a new Laurel that somehow pleased him even more than the one he had seen before.

Hollis bumbled on, "Come right in. Take this chair. No, no. Not interrupting at all. Captain Ledyard and I had quite finished." Almost mechanically Laurel bowed to Grant and allowed herself to be installed in a wing chair near the desk.

Still holding the plate she looked from her uncle to Grant. "Really — I didn't know you were busy, Uncle Jethro. I brought you some fresh doughnuts made this morning." She slid the plate onto the desk, and then sat very straight in the big chair, her slippers barely touching the floor. Her hands were properly folded in her lap.

Hollis cried, "Fresh doughnuts! Now this was thoughtful of you, my dear. Come, Ledyard, you must have some, too, to bless the plate."

As he helped himself, Grant was suddenly aware of Laurel's eyes on him and he became uncomfortably conscious of his uniform, of his jutting sword hilt. Hollis rattled the plate, pulled out his watch and cried with bluff heartiness, "Ledyard, I'm impressed by what you want to do, but as a man of the world you'll see it's not advisable. Now if you'll excuse me — "

Laurel slipped out of the room under cover of Grant's farewells to her uncle. Grant managed to overtake her by the open front door and to step down onto the porch with her. "I had hoped to talk for a little with you, too, Laurel. I've been trying to make your uncle see that certain things ought to be done. I know that he sets great store by you and if you'd back up what I said to him — " He told her of the plight of the burned-out coastal people, concluding, "It would take so little on the part of the state. And it would mean so much to those people."

Her face was puzzled. "These people — they're civilians?"

"Of course."

"And you — you came here to ask Uncle Jethro to help them? It isn't because you want to make soldiers out of them?"

"Soldiers? Hardly. What I don't want to see is a lot of old people, women and children without shelter or food. We're well into September and winter will come rolling down those hills before too long."

There was a new look in her eyes as she said, "Of course I'll help. When you hear of any really bad cases, tell me about them. Then I can go to Uncle Jethro and say, 'Here are some more people who need help.'"

"Accompanying your request with some fresh doughnuts, I hope."

Her dimples showed and her teeth flashed in a quick smile. A maltese kitten scampered across the grass, bounced stiff-legged about Grant's boots. He caught it up, popped it into the inside of his helmet where it alternately purred and chewed at his fingers.

He cautiously moved a step toward the drive and Laurel followed beside him.

They were nearing the stables where Grant's black waited, still saddled. A handsome roan thrust his head from a loose box and whinnied. "That's mine," said Laurel proudly, stroking the soft muzzle. "Uncle gave her to me."

Grant examined the mare approvingly. "Be good over rough country, I'd say." His approval deepened as they entered the stable where four other horses switched their tails meditatively. Grant thought enviously of the advantages of belonging to the Assembly.

It was killing work in the cavalry to mount a few troopers on poor animals and here was a horse fit for the Commander himself. Deeper in the stable, other horses stirred. Jethro Hollis had horses, even though the cavalry lacked them. Well, why not? An Assemblyman was at the beck and call of his people and would have to be ready to answer any demand made on his time.

Grant looked down at the kitten which seemed to have taken complete possession of the helmet where it purred loudly. Laurel, eyes dancing, tickled the kitten's nose with a straw which brought on a flurry of quick-batting paws.

Grant spoke impulsively. "Laurel, can't you forget about this blasted uniform? If it weren't for that, you wouldn't be forever looking at me through a screen of icicles. Barring the uniform you don't exactly dislike being with me, do you? Like the time at Black Rock?"

Her color deepened. "I do wish that you weren't in uniform, and that you never had been." Her voice was steady and cold. Calmly she removed the kitten from his helmet, holding its gray fur against her face.

Grant stepped to the black mare and untethered her. "Good-by Laurel," he said soberly.

Laurel inclined her head gravely over the kitten. "Good-by," she called. "Don't forget about — you know — those lists that you're going to send me."

"I won't," answered Grant. As he rode on toward the Sound, Grant's mind was full of Laurel and his talk with her, this new and still more appealing Laurel who slipped into her uncle's study aproned and carrying a plate of doughnuts.

VI

In Enemy Country

WHEN he reached the Oxbow, Grant turned his horse into the stable yard for the boys to look after and ran up to Tallmadge's room. The major called cheerily in answer to his knock and Grant threw open the door. In the middle of the room Tallmadge carefully adjusted the lace fall of a civilian's light-brown coat, while Caleb Brewster watched him glumly. "Hello!" said the major to Grant. "Did you get what you wanted from Hollis?"

"I doubt it. What are you doing out of uniform? Resigning?"

Tallmadge smiled. "Taking a little trip where I'll see lots of civilians, so I thought I'd dress like them." He glanced at Brewster. "I'm afraid Caleb doesn't approve."

The gunner flushed. "Damned if I do."

Grant looked suspiciously at him. "What's afoot?"

"Steady," said Tallmadge. "This is unofficial. Say nothing about this trip till you have leave from me. I'll be gone for two or three days and I want you to stay right here until I come back. That takes precedence over everything."

Caleb shook his head. "This is all wrong, I tell you."

"You said that before, Caleb. By the way, Grant, have you heard the name John Anderson mentioned since I last saw you?"

"I'd have told you if I had. Look here, sir. I don't know what Caleb's objecting to, but it seems to me that I ought to know a little more before you leave."

"When I come back. You'll see why later. Better — what's that down in the street?"

Grant stepped to the front window. A squad of troopers was

coming on at a smart trot. They wore black, red-banded helmets with foxtails dangling behind, white jackets faced with red, and yellow leather breeches. "A detail from the Commander's guard," Grant said. "They're pulling up here."

"I'll go down and see what they want," growled Brewster. His heavy tread sounded on the stairs, died away, returned. He swung in through the door, a paper in hand. "For you, Major," he said.

Tallmadge opened the letter and began to read, his face expressionless. Then he folded the paper, thrust it into his pocket and began striding up and down the room, eyes on the floor. Grant sat uneasily on the sill while Brewster in his chair jiggled his foot nervously.

The major faced about unexpectedly in his walk. "Caleb," he said, "the Commander agrees with you."

The front legs of Brewster's tipped-back chair struck the floor with a sharp rap. "By God, he's right and I'll bet my head on it. That's all over, then. I'm off for Black Rock and my whaleboats."

"Steady, Caleb. Listen to the last line of the letter. It's in holograph, so I guess he means it. He says, 'I'm writing, to reinforce most earnestly what I gave you verbally. On no account are you to carry out this plan yourself. To this I hold you strictly accountable."

Brewster held out his hands, palms up. "That does it."

"Does what?" asked Grant irritably. "You two are about as talkative as Cradle Rock."

"I hadn't quite finished," said Tallmadge. "The concluding line is, 'The plan must be implemented by such other means as you may best advise.'" He faced Grant. "This plan was mine. I was going to do it myself. The Commander forbids me to go. Also, he says it must be done. I want you to listen carefully and then see if you'll volunteer to take my place."

Grant felt a chill creeping up his back and his mouth went suddenly dry. "Go ahead."

"Someone," said Tallmadge, seating himself astride a chair and leaning his elbows on the back, "someone is wanted, a clever, observant, intelligent, adaptable someone to go across the Sound."

Grant blew his cheeks in relief. "Is that all? I'm none of those adjectives but of course I'll go. Why not? Caleb makes the trip often enough."

"This isn't just a trip across the Sound and back. If you go, you'll wear this suit of mine. You'll be put ashore near Oyster Bay. You'll make your way to Raynham Hall. You do not know the owner, but you do know his son, Culper. The father is Samuel Townsend."

"Again, why not?" asked Grant. "Also what do I do when I get there?"

"The man who goes will merely stay there, keep his eyes and ears and mind open. He will also keep his person free so that if his visit becomes monotonous, he may be able to leave — and at once."

"Hold on a minute," put in Grant. "Just where is Oyster Bay?"

"West down the coast from Setauket, where the Sound gets narrower," said the major. "It is, in effect, a British garrison as there are a good many troops, British and Hessian and Tory nearby. The man who goes will meet one or two people there whom he has already met. There will be others of whom he may have heard but has not met. Sometimes members of Sir Henry Clinton's staff are present, and even Sir Henry himself."

Grant listened as Tallmadge talked on. He could feel the cold creeping up his back again, felt his cheek muscles stiffening and his jaws clenching harder and harder. When he spoke, he found it difficult to get the words out. "I'm to go to Townsend's in civilian clothes and stay there until I've heard enough to make the venture worth-while. Is that it?"

"I particularly did *not* say you," said Tallmadge. "The man who goes."

Brewster burst out. "Look here, Major, whether you go or Grant goes or my uncle's black hinny goes, the risk's too high. What do you say, Grant?"

Grant shook his head silently. When he had left Culper's house in New York, his status had been that of a spy — an officer in an enemy town out of uniform. But somehow that had been different. Now, he was asked to enter the Townsend house boldly, in broad daylight and unsponsored. He was to mix with any number of British officers and Hessians and Tories. He had known dozens of British, met as prisoners or under a flag of truce. The Long Island Tories came from every state. A Worcester man, or a former tutor might be encountered there at Oyster Bay. Not only was the risk great, but he himself was not qualified for such a misson. Hell and death! Didn't Nat Hale, Tallmadge's classmate and close friend, try the same thing back in '76 and end up with a hangman's noose about his neck? Surely Tallmadge must have forgotten about Nat Hale. Then he saw the major's profile against the light. Benjamin Tallmadge had not forgotten. More than that, he had been quietly ready to go himself until the arrival of the Commander's letter. Grant glanced at Brewster, "What tide do you want to catch, Caleb?" he asked. "Major, those civilian clothes of yours will fit me well enough."

That night Grant crouched in the bow of the whaleboat. The light fog that had risen after sundown muffled sound as well as sight, and he could barely hear the soft swirl of the oars as Brewster's crew sent the craft cautiously ahead. The hush was uncanny, frightening. He shivered and drew his cloak tighter about him. The wall of fog grew darker, thicker. Suddenly the shore loomed close and trees took shape against the sky where faint stars glowed. Aft by the tiller he made out Brewster's bulk, an arm raised in signal.

A harsh voice barked, "Good God!" and the eerie hush of the night was broken. Grant felt the keel grate on the sand, heard Brewster shout, "Jump for it!" just as another voice, somewhere out in the foggy distance yelled, *"Wer da?"* Grant gave a wild leap, landed in a half crouch on damp, yielding sand. The whaleboat was rapidly melting into the haze that hung over the water and beyond him men were shouting in German. The whaleboat vanished, reappeared as a ball of lurid fire gushed from its bow and the swivel gun crashed at some target that he couldn't see. There were more flashes, followed by the flat smack of muskets, then silence fell again.

Grant looked wildly about him, feeling completely helpless. He took a deep breath and sternly arranged his thoughts. The first part of his mission had been accomplished. He was safely landed and no one had seen him come ashore. If Brewster had found the right beach, there should be a shingled hut where lobster pots were stored not far above the high water mark. He studied the terrain carefully, but no slanting roof showed anywhere. He threw back his shoulders and strode forward.

Bushes crackled under his feet and coils of dry seaweed rasped his ankles. Suddenly some twenty yards away a man moved cautiously toward him. Grant saw that his cocked hat was bobbing from side to side as though its wearer were peering out to sea. The man stopped and Grant crouched lower. Then a voice he remembered called, "Better head this way, Ledyard. The hut's over here."

Grant ran forward. "Austin Roe! By God, I'm glad to see you."

"I know what you mean," said Roe with a dry laugh. "Let's get going. I've got a cleaning kit to freshen up your shoes and there are some extra silk stockings in my saddle bags."

"That's good. Wait a minute though. What about Brewster? You heard the shots?"

"Plenty," answered Roe. "But he'll be all right. That must have been a patrol boat with Hessians aboard. This way. We want to make Townsend's place by daybreak."

Roe led the way along a path that climbed the hummocks and then wound away over a great stretch of flat country. Grant hurried on in his wake. "Look here, Roe, how the devil did you know I'd be the one to land?" he asked.

"Had to be you. We figured it so in New York," said Roe over his shoulder as he plunged ahead into an oak grove. Grant followed, checking a whistle of admiration. There stood the same fine-limbed horse that Roe had picked up at Onderdonk's and beyond it, two matched grays were hitched to a phaeton. On the box a fattish man turned and gathered the reins.

"Ledyard," Roe said, "this is Abel Gilman, a friend of a friend of ours in New York."

Gilman dropped from the box and shook hands with Grant. "So it's you that's going? Mister, that's a job I wouldn't — "

"No job at all," cut in Grant. "I'm just looking in on the father of a friend of mine."

Gilman nodded slowly. "Guess that's the smart way to figure it. Ready to go, Austin?"

"Ready. Get in, Ledyard. Here's your cleaning kit and fresh stockings."

Grant changed his stockings and applied the brush that Roe tossed him. The latter paced his mount beside Grant as Gilman started his team. "All spruce now, Ledyard? Take these papers. They show that you crossed at Brooklyn Ferry yesterday, that you laid over last night at Onderdonk's. Here's a letter from Sir Henry Clinton, addressed to Grant Ledyard, Esq., No. 5 Broadway. You're buying hay for him. Can you talk hay?"

Grant tucked the papers in his pocket. "I can talk hay. But look here. These papers are in my name. What would you have done if someone else had come?"

"I tell you, it had to be you," said Roe. "If it hadn't been — well, I'd have burned the papers and trusted to my tongue. It would probably have been all right, though. There's a good chance we won't have to show them." He trotted up abreast of the grays.

For the moment, Grant dared relax. He should have known that his reception on Long Island would be carefully thought out, even to the papers. He wondered just how the British commander had been induced to write the letter and just who he thought Grant Ledyard, Esq., of No. 5 Broadway was. No doubt it had been done as a favor for good old Rob Townsend.

Day was coming on and smoke curled lazily from farm chimneys. A boy with a broad, Dutch face stared at the phaeton as he filled a bucket at a spring. Not only the farms were astir. Drums muttered in the fields to the right and left where tents raised their brownish cones. Mounted Jaegers in little cocked hats and green jackets led horses out to water. Beyond them the brass helmets of a detail of the 17th Dragoons flashed in the sun.

By a crossroad, the phaeton ground to a halt as a sergeant and a guard detail blocked the road. The sergeant began questioning Gilman. On impulse, Grant picked up the long, silver-headed stick that he had brought from Fairfield and tapped the sergeant on his epaulet. "Look sharp, my man," he said languidly. "You're delaying me."

The sergeant glared, then turned to Austin Roe. "Who's he?" he asked.

Roe glanced sourly at Grant. "Got a letter from Sir Henry-bloody-Clinton and he thinks he's God on his golden throne."

The sergeant's expression changed. "I'll have to ask to see the letter, sir," he said with cautious firmness, while he eyed Grant's civilian coat and its silver buttons with obvious respect. Grant picked out the letter and tossed it to him. The man read it carefully, then handed it back. "No offense, sir. Orders is strict. You'll not hold this against me?"

Grant waved regally. "Not at all. Doing your duty, I'm sure. Look here, postilion!" he called to Roe. "You are supposed to attend to these matters for me. If you'd had your wits about you, you wouldn't have wasted my time and that of this good fellow here."

Roe glowered at him, gave his hat a surly touch. "Very good, your Honor."

"Look to it," said Grant coldly. "And give this man a shilling. Driver, proceed."

As the phaeton moved on past the grateful sergeant and his men, Roe pulled alongside Grant. "You're doing fine. You handled that sergeant just right."

The road swung toward the Sound, climbed a broad, shallow

hill. On the crest, Grant looked down on a deep, irregular bay with groves of oaks and chestnuts and maples along the shore. Abel Gilman pointed with his whip. "See that stand of sycamore? The roof behind it is Raynham Hall, Mr. Samuel Townsend's place."

Grant closed his eyes as though mustering all his faculties. When he opened them again, the phaeton was rolling along an elm-shaded street. Women chattered across garden fences. There were no empty cellarholes here, no stark chimneys or fire-blackened walls. The people seemed at ease and their eyes did not turn seaward in anxious questioning as did eyes in Fairfield.

Gilman pulled in beside a low white house that stood back from the road and Grant stepped down from the carriage. His heart contracted and he clutched his stick. He stumbled, recovered himself and mind and vision cleared as he took in the scene before him.

A young, handsome British major leaned on the sill of an upper window and called down to a pretty brown-haired girl who laughed up at him, her arms full of flowers.

The front door opened and a tall, white-haired man came down the flagged path. Grant saw old, shrewd eyes behind silver-bowed spectacles, saw a firm mouth relax in a smile. "May I be of service to you, sir?" asked the old man.

Grant bowed. "Am I addressing Mr. Samuel Townsend, sir?"

"Yes," he said. "Come in." He swung open the gate.

Grant tucked his hat under his arm and bowed. "I am Grant Ledyard with a letter from Sir Henry Clinton. He's concerned about his reserves of hay and has asked me to see one or two of the leading men on Long Island about it." He handed Clinton's letter to Mr. Townsend. "This will vouch for me."

The old man opened the letter and settled his spectacles. "H'm. Of course, of course. Glad to oblige, I'm sure. I'd heard rumors that some of his purchases were hardly up to the mark. Burdock and dandelion instead of good sound timothy and clover. Yes, I'd heard." He handed the letter back to Grant. "So your mission is not altogether unexpected, you see. But you know, if I were Sir Henry, I'd keep a better guard of what's already in his depots, fodder for man as well as for beast. Why, take Coram, take Hempstead. A smart raid from across the Sound could be costly to him. You'll drop a word about those places?"

Grant tried to keep his face impassive. Culper's father had been expecting him, or his equivalent, and was telling him that a force in Caleb Brewster's whaleboats might find worthwhile objectives on Long Island. He answered carelessly, "I'll leave a hint in the proper quarters."

"I'm sure you will. Now as to this hay matter. Your time's your own? Then you'd better spend a day or two with me. No trouble at all. I've plenty of room and you'll find some stirring young people running in and out, capital chaps, all of them."

As Abel Gilman drew out a stout valise from under the seat and hurried around to a side door with it, Grant followed his host up the flagged walk. The major at the upper window was leaning still farther over the sill, flourishing a piece of paper as he declaimed:

> *Dare I smite my humble lyre*
> *In praise of Sarah, fresh and fair?*
> *Should I fear that she might tire*
> *Or deem that praise a* ruse de guerre?

The girl laughed. "But that's the same verse you dedicated to Polly Morgan! All you've done is change the name. Now, John, if you really mean — " She stopped as she caught sight of Mr. Townsend and Grant.

The old man smiled at her and the boyish major. "Sarah, you might tell him that so far he hasn't begun to rival that valentine that Colonel Simcoe sent you."

The major crumpled up his paper. "This, sir, is too much. First Sarah interrupts me and misses my finest lines. Then you throw

John Simcoe's balderdash at me, his limping meter and his bad rhymes."

Mr. Townsend chuckled. "They pleased Sarah and that's the main test. Sarah, my dear, this is Mr. Grant Ledyard, who is staying with us for a day or two. Mr. Ledyard, my daughter, Sarah. As to the aspiring bard at the window, you've probably seen him in New York — Sir Henry Clinton's adjutant general, Major John André."

Sarah curtsied to Grant, who bowed to her, then to the major. "I've not the honor of the major's acquaintance. This is the first time I've had a chance to help Sir Henry."

André cocked his elbows on the sill. "What? You're doing something for the old buffer? Something scandalous, I hope."

"Nothing more romantic than hay," answered Grant.

"Oh, on the commissary side are you? That's out of my province, quite." A mischievous glint came into his bright eyes. "You know, I'm really playing truant from Sir Henry and I like it so much that I'm not sure I'm going back to him." He looked sidewise at Sarah. "How would you like it, if I just stayed here and penned verses to you?"

She raised doubtful eyebrows. "That would depend on how many names you'd scratched out of those verses before you put mine in."

"Oh but my dear girl!" André protested. "Don't you see that if I scratch out ten thousand, then that means you are superior to ten thousand."

"There's something rather Turkish in your reasoning, Major," Grant remarked. "But I agree this is a much pleasanter spot than any headquarters. Has your truancy lasted long?"

"A week or more. Tell me, when you last saw Sir Henry, didn't you think he looked more than usually harassed?"

"In the very depths, though of course I couldn't have known that it was due to the absence of his adjutant general," said Grant. A week or more away from headquarters! That meant that the major must have been absent when Grant's papers were contrived.

André beamed. "In the depths, is he? Ha! I shall play him like a trout, sir. I shall exact all sorts of special privileges when I do report to him. Now tell me about yourself. You're staying here?"

Samuel Townsend cut in gently. "Yes, just as soon as I can get him out of the garden and into his room."

"Staying here?" Sarah's quick, bright smile warmed Grant. "Oh, how nice that is for us. Father, he can squire Polly Morgan!"

"And you shall take wine with me before lunch, Mr. Ledyard," exclaimed André. "My dear Sarah, I'll set to work at once on some more verses for you!" With a bow and a smile he vanished from the window.

Grant's room, fresh with flowered curtains and coverlet, was diagonally across the house from André's. One set of windows looked down toward the bay. Another showed a wide sweep of the drive and a corner of the stables. As Grant drew clean linen and a more elaborate stock from his valise that had been brought up before him, he tried to size up the house and its inhabitants. It was obvious that Samuel Townsend kept open house, willingly or unwillingly, for British officers and their Tory and Hessian colleagues.

He thought of what Tallmadge had told him of Culper's fears. Something ominous was brewing, but no hint had been given of its nature. Samuel Townsend had had no special word for him, although he had expected a guest from the other side of the Sound. As to the other guest, Major John André, Grant was puzzled. He had a feeling that André's presence was accidental and unforeseen. But he would have to be watched as any enemy officer must be watched.

Hoofs crunched on the drive. Past a corner of the house Grant saw a couple of orderlies in the green of the Queen's Rangers leading a riderless horse toward the stables. Then he heard a buzz of voices on the lawn at the far end of the house.

Still Grant stood by the window, waiting. Then he turned, caught up a silver snuffbox that he had found in his valise, gave a last touch to the lace at his cuffs and went down the broad stairs, running his fingers lightly along the mahogany railing.

The sunny dining room at the right of the stairs was empty, but its long table was set for several people. At the far end a door opened onto a stretch of smooth lawn where André stood by a sideboard covered with bottles and glasses. Sarah was close by him, giving her hand to a square-faced, blunt-featured Ranger colonel. Behind the colonel a pleasant-faced lieutenant, carrying the cylindrical busby of Emmerick's dragoons under his arm, bowed from the waist.

Grant paused. The colonel must be the same Colonel Simcoe of whom Tallmadge had spoken and surely the same whose valentine to Sarah had been mentioned by Samuel Townsend. The lieutenant was obviously one of Knyphausen's Hessians attached to Emmerick's Tory command, for his English, while good enough, was stilted and heavily Teutonic. For the moment, Grant could see no danger to himself from either of these men, since in their eyes he would be sponsored by André.

Then he saw another girl standing near Sarah, a slim girl with very dark hair, bright black eyes, a tip-tilted nose and lips that curved in a quick smile. She must be the Polly Morgan of whom Sarah and the major had spoken. Then he forgot about the girl as he saw the civilian, short and stocky in a brick-red coat, with whom she was talking. There could be no mistake. Dan Boyce, who had roomed near him in Massachusetts Hall during his freshman year! Grant had lost sight of him in '76, but had heard of Dan's joining a company sponsored by Israel Putnam. What could Dan be doing here, and out of uniform? Could he, too, have known a man in New York who signed himself as Samuel Culper?

Grant had not noticed the step down onto the grass and he stumbled. André caught him by the arm, crying gaily, " 'For many men that stumble at the threshold are well foretold that danger lurks within.' " The Hessian looked puzzled and André went on. "Just a tag from *King Henry VI*. No application here."

"Very pat," said Grant. "Of course you might have used the line, 'Wishing his foot were equal with his eye.'"

André clapped him on the shoulder. "Right! It begins:

> 'Like one that stands upon a promontory
> And spies a far-off shore where he would tread.'

It's from the same act."

Grant winced. Had the major chosen his lines at random, or did they hold mocking assurance that his mission was known? He kept a fixed smile on his face as André presented him to the Ranger, Colonel Simcoe, and the Hessian, von Kittel. Then André cried, "Bless my bones! You haven't met our most charming neighbor. Polly, my dear, do let me present this most delightful guest. Miss Polly Morgan, Mr. Grant Ledyard."

Grant bowed. "A neighbor, Miss Morgan?"

The black eyes smiled up at him. "I live quite close by. Sarah tells me that you may stay here a day or two. I do hope so."

"Indeed, I plan to," answered Grant quickly. "But I must be about my business as soon as I've changed my sea legs for land legs."

The smile was gone from Polly's eyes and she bit her lip. Then she laughed. "Surely, Mr. Ledyard, you can't treat just crossing the East River as a sea voyage."

Grant stiffened inwardly, shot a hurried glance at the others. To his vast relief, they were all chatting among themselves, paying no attention to him and the girl. He turned to Polly again, saw that she was still smiling, but that a deep concern for him underlay her expression. Somehow, he knew that she was aware of at least the general nature of his business at Raynham Hall. Recovering himself, he answered, "But my dear Miss Morgan, the way the East River ferries run these days! Crossing to Brooklyn is the equivalent of that voyage to England we'd all like to take."

Her tone was natural again as she said, "I'm sure that you'll manage ferries perfectly well along with your business. Have you met Mr. Boyce?"

Boyce stepped forward, but showed no trace of recognition. "I heard you exchanging quotations with the major, Mr. Ledyard. You've been to a college? I envy you."

"Oh, that," answered Grant, deprecatingly. "The major hit on about the only line I know. Yes, I had a year at Harvard."

André's gay voice cut in as he appeared with wine glasses on a tray. "I'm playing Ganymede. Sarah, Polly, you have your glasses? Take one, Mr. Ledyard. I know you were being modest about your accomplishments, so complete this tag if you can: 'For in my youth I never did apply hot and rebellious liquors to my blood.'"

"I wasn't being modest, Major. And I can only say that this wine was never rebellious. It's as sound and loyal as Sir Henry himself. Otherwise, I'm sure that no one here would drink it."

Colonel Simcoe set his glass down with a rap. "That's a sentiment that would vouch for you in any honest company, Mr. Ledyard. Rebel! Rebellious!" He grated out two words with cold anger.

Boyce looked at him quizzically. "You won't allow that some to whom those words applied may be merely misguided, Colonel?"

"Misguided?" snapped Simcoe. "Rot 'em, no! Nothing but sheer, black treason, top to bottom." Simcoe flushed angrily and burst into a heated denunciation of all rebels while Grant watched with covert interest. If Boyce were playing a part, he was doing it very well, establishing himself as a reasonable man but a loyal one. But the sound course was to wait until Boyce showed his hand.

Later, Grant found himself seated between André and Polly at the long table, with the young Hessian directly across from him. Conversation had become general. He began to experience a feeling of senseless bravado. He began to ask questions about military matters, questions such as might occur to any well-intentioned civilian. Many of these, Simcoe and André answered frankly, but the information would have been of little value across the Sound.

Von Kittel's guttural tones caught his ear. "So — all his baggage we take, all his papers so official. It was when I rode with your de Lancey. Ach, It was such fun!"

"What was fun?" asked André, leaning forward.

"In Westchester where we chase the rebel Tallmadge, Herr Major."

Grant was instantly alert. "When was this, Lieutenant?" He hoped that his voice sounded steady.

"Oh, it is some months!" replied von Kittel.

Grant smothered a sigh of relief. No new disaster had touched Tallmadge.

"A smart piece of work," observed Simcoe. "There was nothing very interesting in those papers, though. Just the same, that damned Tallmadge will bear watching."

"Perhaps you'll try again, Lieutenant," said Polly, smiling at the Hessian.

Simcoe grunted. "Maybe the lieutenant won't have time to try —unless he hurries." He glanced meaningly at André.

André's fingers were about his glass. His hand jerked and wine slopped over onto the table cloth. He gave a high, nervous laugh.

Simcoe snatched up his fork again, muttering, "Well, well!" in an irritated tone, as though he had caught himself in some breach of etiquette. André turned to Grant. "May I trouble you for a pinch of salt, Mr. Ledyard? That's it. Just spread it over the wine stain. My dear hostess and chatelaine of Raynham Hall, this cloth will emerge as spotless as your complexion. My hand behaved like a clumsy tavern oaf's."

Grant worked the salt back and forth across the stain, trying to keep outwardly calm while his mind raced. Simcoe and André knew of some impending move of such importance, so secret, that the vaguest hint of its existence had for an instant shattered André's smooth poise. As Grant swept away the last of the salt, a general scraping of chairs broke into his thought. Samuel Townsend was addressing him.

"If it's your pleasure, Mr. Ledyard, we'll drive about the country in my chaise and talk to a few of the people who may help in this hay matter."

Grant hesitated. His impulse was to stay as close as possible to André and Simcoe, but a second glance at his host's expression made him change his mind.

Through the long afternoon drive, Samuel Townsend chatted on amiably to Grant. For nearly four years his house had been a virtual headquarters for the British troops quartered in that section of Long Island. At the present moment Simcoe was using it as a sort of executive base from which he started his tours of inspection. Unofficially, it had been a great rendezvous for the young officers, many of whom came clear from Manhattan to pay harmless court to Sarah and Polly. Wild young bloods some of them, but John Simcoe made them toe the mark and the girls were too sensible, thank God, to take any of them seriously.

Grant listened as he watched the green countryside slide past. Once or twice he tried guardedly to turn the conversation to more specific channels, but his advances were blandly ignored. When they stopped at a farm or a warehouse, his host plunged at once into the business at hand and Grant soon became aware that hay was actually being contracted for, that the fifty tons inspected here or the two hundred stored far down the Jericho road would be duly forwarded to Manhattan.

Gradually, the wisdom of Samuel Townsend grew on him. If others were to believe in Grant's role, he himself must believe it. He must be an expert on hay. He threw himself into his role energetically, coldly rejecting low quality fodder, badgering farmers into unearthing hidden stores of higher quality. When at sunset they finally turned back toward Oyster Bay, the old man gave an approving nod. "You've a fine eye, Mr. Ledyard. I think you've attended to this business very well. Your superiors ought to be pleased." He smiled. "You're like my son, Rob — and by the way I hope that you'll look in on him when you return to New York. Rob's a born merchant and he doesn't feel that he's really carried out an order until he's followed it right down to actual delivery. Now you've contracted for this hay, but you won't feel you're done until you've seen every last wisp safe in Sir Henry's stables."

"H'm," said Grant. "Something like that. Just the same —"

"Does you credit," cut in the old man heartily, as the roof of Raynham Hall showed above the sycamores. "Now I'll leave you at the gate. I want to go down to the bay to see some of the oystermen."

Grant got out of the chaise with a word of thanks and walked toward the garden where Polly was looking approvingly at the neat flower beds. She looked up. "Good evening, Mr. Ledyard," she called as he came through the white gate.

Grant took off his high Kevenhuller. "Good evening to you." He lowered his voice. "Has any word or message come for me?"

"For you, Mr. Ledyard?" Polly's dark eyes showed only polite interest. "I'm quite sure not. No one's come to the house since you and Mr. Townsend left. Sarah and I have been right here." She began to move up the path.

"By your smile, I'd say you'd had more verses written to you," ventured Grant.

Polly tossed her dark head. "Oh that John André! If there isn't a girl around, he hymns the moon or the house cat. He just can't help it."

"You told me that you were a neighbor, Miss Morgan," said Grant. "Perhaps you'll allow me to pay my respects to you and your family before I leave."

Polly's black eyes widened. "Oh, didn't you know? I'm staying here for a little while, visiting Sarah. I live alone with my brother and he's gone down to Great South Bay for a few days. I'm sorry he's not here. You'd like each other."

"He's a soldier, perhaps?" ventured Grant.

"No. He's a little lame, so he — well, he does the same sort of work that you're doing. Now if you'll excuse me, I've got to go in and help Sarah."

Grant climbed slowly to his room, pondering over her words.

"He does the same sort of work that you're *doing.*" Not 'that you *do.*' How much did Polly Morgan know or guess?

Hot water had been placed on the washstand beyond the bed, and fresh towels were draped over a rack. Beyond the barns a cow lowed. Some boys playing in a pasture screeched and called to each other. Creaking wheels and a hoarse horn told of the passage of a fish peddler. Late in the day though it was, bees hummed somewhere nearby.

Grant dropped his towel and stood motionless, holding his breath. The buzzing rise and fall kept on, seemingly coming out of the wall behind the washstand. Not bees. Voices. He stepped nearer to the wall, one hand on the faded paper that gave slightly to his touch. At some time in the past, Raynham Hall had been altered and from the opening in his fireplace, a new chimney had been run up. He could see where an older chimney had been abandoned and its fireplace hastily sealed. Up the disused flue from the room below came voices, throbbing and muttering, faint in spots, louder and clearer where only paper covered a forgotten gap.

Grant pressed his ear against the spot, his heart racing. Gradually, the vague sounds took form. In the room below him, Simcoe and André were talking, the colonel's voice heavy and rather surly, the major's higher and musical. They seemed to be walking up and down for the voices died, swelled, died only to swell again. Now the colonel was speaking. "I say again, I don't like it. And I don't see what it will accomplish."

André's voice was urgent. "Look at all this area. See how everything hinges around it. Beginning here — "

Grant clenched his fists in exasperation as the two apparently moved out of earshot. The paper under his ear was deadly silent. He pressed closer. It was Simcoe again. "Maybe something in what you say. But when you've got here — " there was a pause as though the colonel were indicating a spot on a map — "where are you?"

André spoke so gently that Grant could barely catch the words.

"Where are we? We're everywhere. It's like splitting a rotten log. And without firing a shot. It'll be all over!"

Once more the voices died. Grant waited. Then a door slammed below and presently he heard André calling gayly to Sarah from the front garden. The unseen colloquy was over.

Grant began to dress mechanically. Something was afoot, something bigger and more desperate than any of Culper's hints. John André, adjutant-general to Sir Henry Clinton, had spoken of some move that would topple everything. Like splitting a rotten log. No shot would be fired. If only he could see the map they had used! Perhaps he might be able to slip into the room below. He discarded the idea. Unless the map were marked it would do him no good.

Settling his silver-buttoned jacket he came down the stairs. His best move was to find Samuel Townsend, ask him the whereabouts of Austin Roe and send an oral report to Robert Townsend. He stepped out into the garden. Leaning on the gate he looked up and down the street hoping for a glimpse of his host, but there was no sign of the chaise.

A hand fell on his shoulder and he turned with a start of alarm. The blunt, snub-nosed face of Dan Boyce looked gravely at him.

"Sorry!" said Grant hastily. "Gave me quite a start. I didn't hear you coming, Mr. Boyce."

Boyce said slowly, "I didn't mean to creep up like that — Grant."

Grant rallied himself. "No apologies — ah — I don't think that our host mentioned your first name," he said smoothly.

Boyce gave a slight smile. "It's been a pleasure to watch you. I somehow would never have thought you fitted for this sort of work. You were rather the type that wants action." He laid a hand on Grant's shoulder. "I tell you, I feel a lot better, knowing that you're working along beside me. A lot better."

"Are you after hay, too?" asked Grant.

"Not hay, exactly," answered Boyce. "Let's say we're both after supplies, tangible or intangible." He lowered his voice. "Any way I can help you?"

"I got most of my work done this afternoon, thanks," said Grant. Boyce kept his voice at a low pitch. "I'm not asking any questions. You do very well to play your cards close. Just remember, I'm here and available if you need help. I'm going to forget that I've seen you. Do the same for me." He pushed away from the gate, his voice at normal level. "I'd say you'd earned Sir Henry's thanks. You must have a way with you to wheedle stores out of these people, even at present prices."

He fell into step with Grant as André appeared around the corner, giving an arm to Polly and Sarah. The major called gaily, "Now we're complete. Come along, you good fellows. I've just made the discovery that neither of these Yankee paragons has tasted frothed chocolate, which I now propose to prepare for them with my own hands. You shall watch and taste with them."

He ushered the girls into the house with a bow. Boyce excused himself, but Grant followed the major. He had a sudden hankering to sample André's chocolate — it would give him a chance to study the man at close range, without risk of detection.

Soon the major was busy with powdered chocolate, spices and hot water, measuring, blending, sniffing, stirring. He kept up a steady stream of amusing comment as he worked, while the girls twitted him on the least slip. A diverting little coxcomb, Grant thought as he studied André. A fop, a macaroni, a bit of airy, harmless fluff. Yet none of those terms fitted the man who had talked so earnestly to Simcoe.

When the girls had been served, André presented a cup to Grant with a dancing master's flourish. The mixture was delicate, rich with an odd spicy tang that was new to Grant. André plunged into a long hymn in praise of chocolate, backing his thesis with quotations in French, Greek and English, then turned to a learned discussion of the current London modes and manners as gleaned from the English press. The room grew dim, but André talked on until the sight of a mounted orderly coming up the drive sent him off with a final verse, flourish and bow. The girls excused themselves, leaving Grant alone with the dregs of the chocolate and his thoughts, which seemed to him almost as muddy. He had spent nearly an hour in the major's company without having learned a single new fact about him or his doings, save that he treated chocolate with masterful respect.

After a late supper, Grant retired to his room where he sat with an ear to the wall, but did not hear even the vaguest whisper from below. At length he went down the stairs, through a silent house, and out into the garden. The shades were drawn in Samuel Townsend's house, but down the road, a single light glowed, soft and yellow. He watched it idly, wondering what interior it lighted. Then something black moved against the golden glow. The black mass resolved itself into two figures outside that house, men in high-cocked hats. For an instant they stood close together, as though talking earnestly. Then one of them came rapidly down the road toward Grant. Soon he recognized the build and gait of his classmate, Boyce. Grant shrank back against a catalpa tree hoping to be out of sight. Turning abruptly down a path that ran outside the fence Dan Boyce headed for the darkened kitchen wing. A door opened and closed, softly but distinctly in the calm night. Then a light flared in the kitchen and a hand drew a curtain. A breeze from the bay rustled the curtain, drew it in, then out almost at right angles to the wall.

Grant stood silently watching. Dan was near a low table that held an earthenware crock. Above it were built-in cupboards. Grant chuckled to himself. "Oh ho, Dan. After a midnight snack, eh?" But Dan seemed to be fumbling with the lower edge of the cupboard. Suddenly his hand drew away a slab of wood, showing a narrow opening in the sill below the cupboard door. He took a white oblong of paper out of his pocket and slid it into the groove, then replaced the slab of wood. Again the kitchen was dark.

Grant stood lost in thought. Why should Dan hide his letter, if that was what he had slid in there? He must have known of the leanings of the Townsend household, might even have known of

Samuel Culper. If that paper was highly secret and confidential, there was no reason why Boyce could not have kept it on his own person, or even turned it over to Samuel Townsend to be locked away in his safe. Dan Boyce had always been a solid, reasonable sort of chap. He surely knew what he was doing and why.

Something moved in the dark ahead of him, in the shadow of a high hedge. He gave a quick side-step and his hand instinctively felt for the hilt of his missing saber. Then a low voice called, "Mr. Ledyard?"

Grant gave a gasp of relief. "Polly Morgan! This is an unexpected pleasure."

She came close to him. "I want to talk to you." Her voice was low and hurried. "Please walk along with me — just as though we were strolling."

Grant offered her his arm. "What's the matter?" he asked.

She shook her head earnestly. "Listen, Mr. Ledyard, what would you think if you heard two men talking about something, a very big something, that would end the war, that would lead to many hangings of rebels?"

Grant said slowly, "I'd think — well — that's all pretty vague."

"No. There's more than just that. They mentioned West Point several times. One of them said, 'It's all arranged.' What could that mean? No — please keep walking."

Grant resumed his pace, his mind whirling. "Why, West Point's the key to all the Colonies. It controls the Hudson. It ties the New England colonies to all the rest. It's — but, good Lord, I'd personally be glad to see an attempt made on West Point. Arnold's in command there now and any British coup would be like sticking your bare foot into a hornet's nest."

"You don't think these men I speak of were serious, then?" asked Polly.

"H'm," Grant rubbed his chin. "They might have been romanticizing."

"But they said, 'It's all arranged,'" said Polly firmly.

125

"Then they're fools. They — " he fell silent. There might be treachery on Arnold's staff. Yes, such a thing was possible, but not probable. Yet — yet — this all seemed to chime in so perfectly with the talk he had half-heard between Simcoe and André. The latter had, Grant thought, been pointing to a map as he talked. Was West Point the missing link in that talk?

"You look at it seriously, then?" asked Polly quietly.

"Yes," answered Grant. He reflected a moment. If there *were* treason at West Point, even a slim chance of it, Samuel Culper should be warned immediately. But how to get word to him? Whom could he trust here? Then he remembered Polly's quick thinking before lunch, her remarks in the garden later in the afternoon. Surely here was the person to help him.

"Polly," he said, "do you know anything about a secret slot in the cabinet above the big kitchen table?"

"A secret slot? Mercy no. And I know this house as well as my own."

"There is one, I'm sure." He stopped, turned to her. "Will you do this for me? Will you go in and see? Press the sill on the left just below the cupboard door. Slide out the loose piece of wood, and I think you'll find a letter."

"Do you want me to bring it to you?"

Grant reflected. It would be more valuable for the moment to find out to whom it was addressed and then who would collect it. Later, other steps might be taken. He said, "Just tell me to whom it's addressed."

Polly flitted off through the night. Grant sat on a milestone and waited. In ten minutes she was back. "Yes," she said, "I found it. Strange. The letter is addressed to a Mr. John Anderson."

"John Anderson!" exclaimed Grant with a violent start.

"What's the matter? Do you know him?"

"No. But I've got to find out who picks up that letter. Is there any spot from where the kitchen could be watched safely?"

Polly thought a minute. "Perhaps the passage to the wellhouse would do. You could go in through the outer door, and if you met anyone, you could pretend you were thirsty and wanted some cold water."

"Good," said Grant. "You are being very helpful, Polly. If anything goes wrong, I'll try to bluster it out." Polly, Grant reflected, was cool and efficient. She had not annoyed him with questions or foolish worries. Instinctively she seemed to know just what to do, how best she could help him.

The wellhouse was cool and dark. Hands before him, Grant moved forward until he felt the rough coping of the well. The passage that led to the kitchen must be directly ahead of him. Leaning against the curb, he settled himself to wait. Once something bumped against his ankles. He reached down and felt an arching, furry back as one of the house cats wove about his feet, purring happily. Glad of the companionship, he set the cat on the cover of the well and stroked its chin while his ears remained alert.

Somewhere a clock struck ten. A thin thread of gold showed low in the darkness and he heard a cautious pad of feet. His hand bumped against a wet-sided bucket, slid on against an empty glass. He filled the glass from the bucket and walked boldly into the passage, heading for the golden thread.

With assumed confidence he pushed the door open, blinking in the light of the single candle that burned on a table to his left. "Good evening, Major," said Grant. "This is a damned fine well our host has here." He raised his glass and drank casually.

Major André in shirt sleeves and slippers, his back toward the room, made a quick motion with his hands and Grant caught a gleam of white paper. When André turned, the paper was gone, and he waved a half-eaten piece of cake. "Join my midnight revels, Mr. Ledyard. You've not tasted our Sarah's spice cake? Then a treat waits you." He turned back to the table, seized a knife and cut a slice from a loaf which lay there.

"Thanks," said Grant, biting into the cake. "This is good, isn't it? Glad I saw your light and came in. That ham we had at dinner left me with a colossal thirst."

"There's some capital Madeira in the sideboard," observed André.

Grant shook his head. "This calls for water."

The two munched on in amity. André bewailed the difficulty of getting really good wines in New York while Grant admired, as he had before, the major's gift of endowing any subject with interest and wit. He found himself wishing he did not know about that letter to Mr. John Anderson now lying hidden behind André's long, red waistcoat.

André smothered a yawn. "I'll have to wish you a good night now," he said. "I've another hour's work on some papers that came in from Sir Henry. Shall I see you in the morning?"

"I hope so, Major," answered Grant. "Please don't bother to light me out. I'm going to stroll about a little more and the path's perfectly clear, even in the dark."

Outside Grant walked swiftly around the house to the little bay window where a candle burned. Polly was bent over a book when he rapped gently on the glass. She put the book down and slipped out through a side door. "Well?" she asked as Grant led her out of earshot."

Grant hesitated. Was he justified in taking her completely into his confidence? Suddenly he pushed aside all doubts. "I've got to send a letter to New York tonight."

"Tonight? That's going to be hard." Her voice dropped. "To Rob?"

So she knew about that! He *had* been right in trusting her! Aloud he said, "Of course. The only question is how."

Polly was silent for a moment. Then she said quickly, "I know a way, a safe way."

"A messenger? Who?"

"Here he comes now." She turned as the front door jarred open and a tall officer in a dragoon's helmet stood framed in the light.

As he closed the door and started down the path, Polly called, "Captain Youngs?"

The dragoon halted and peered into the darkness. "Who — Jove, it's Polly! I wondered if I'd have a chance to see you. Colonel Simcoe's been talking my head off for the last hour."

She laughed. "I saw you ride up after dinner, Daniel. You'll be at our tea day after tomorrow, won't you?"

"The Lord and Sir Henry willing."

"Then will you do me a favor — you're going back now? It's for that tea. Oh — I forgot. You two haven't met, have you? Captain Youngs of the 17th and Mr. Grant Ledyard, on business for Sir Henry."

The two men murmured acknowledgments while Polly went on. "Daniel, there's a special kind of tea that Rob Townsend manages to get us. If you're riding to New York tonight, would you take a note to him about it? Then his agent, Roe, or whatever his name is, can bring us a box or two."

"Be a pleasure," said Youngs, touching his helmet. "I'll go right past Rob's and if I haven't time to stop, I'll send my sergeant in with it. Is the letter ready?"

"I'll write it now. How soon do you start?"

"Half an hour. I'll send a trooper for it." He bowed and went clanking out of the garden.

"Lucky I remembered he came in after supper," Polly said. "He'll go straight back to New York."

"But," said Grant slowly, "have you thought what could happen if he, or someone else read that letter?"

"I'll put my seal on it. He'd never think of breaking that. Let's go in. We haven't much time. We'll use Mr. Townsend's study. The officers don't come into that part of the house after dinner unless they're asked. Come along. Through this door."

Standing by a high, slanting desk, she dipped a quill in a pewter inkstand. On impulse, Grant gently took the pen from her. "I'd better write this," he said. "If this letter should be found in your handwriting, awkward questions could be asked, awkward for a good many people. But how about the tea?"

"Oh, we've plenty of that in the pantry."

Grant nodded, then wrote rapidly, summarizing his news. A catastrophe threatening West Point, with a strong suggestion of treason. A letter to John Anderson picked up by John André. The door creaked and he gave a violent start. Samuel Townsend stood in the entrance, spectacles on his forehead. "Can I help?" he asked.

Polly answered quickly. "A letter to Rob about tea. Captain Youngs will deliver it."

"I thought so," said the old man. "You're not giving Rob much time, are you?"

"He'll know how to manage," said Grant, sanding his letter.

Polly took the sheet, folded it and sealed it. "This will — Listen! There's Youngs's trooper. He's early. I'll slip out and give it to him."

"And now," said Samuel Townsend, "about yourself. You'd better leave at once."

"I've been wondering about that, sir. I'll be missed."

"André and Simcoe are leaving early tomorrow to inspect some camps. They'll not be surprised to find you gone when they come back."

"But Dan Boyce?"

Townsend smiled. "You did very well with him. He thinks that you and he are working together. He told me so. But to return to you. From several things I gathered something was up. So I reasoned that you might want to be off as soon as possible. I've sent for Abel Gilman. Remember that ruined stone house I pointed out to you during our drive? He'll be waiting there with a chaise. Your papers'll see you through the camps, but beyond that, anything might happen. It's bad Tory country. Abel will leave you on the west bank of the Nissequogue River, a few miles this side of Setauket. A man there will tell you how to get across the Sound."

Grant looked at the old man in admiration. "I must say, sir, that you're able to improvise mighty quick."

"We often have to. It's habit. Now off with you. Don't worry about your valise. I'll see that it's hidden."

Grant left the desk reluctantly. "I suppose I'd better hurry. I'd hoped to have a chance to say good-by to Polly. She's done so much."

"I sympathize with your reluctance to go," smiled Mr. Townsend. "I'll make your adieu for you — though doubtless not so eloquently as you would have. Good night and good luck."

Grant went out the rear door, skirted the wall of the vegetable garden and made his way to the road. Something hummed lightly past his ear and landed ahead of him with a little thud. He turned quickly and saw a girl running toward him. "You forgot this," Polly whispered, holding out Tallmadge's long, silver-headed stick. "It was leaning up against the fence."

Grant caught it up. It would probably have remained there till morning when someone would have found it. Had André or Simcoe noticed it they might have wondered that so careful a person as one Grant Ledyard, who contracted for hay in Sir Henry Clinton's name, could have forgotten it — unless it had been overlooked in a hasty, forced flight. "You're clever, Polly," he said. "Not only bringing this, but flipping a pebble past me instead of calling. I hope some day the country can know all about what you people here are doing." He quickly caught her hand, kissed it and, with a finger to his hat, started off.

Some hours later, Abel Gilman halted the chaise in the midst of a stretch of moorlike country where the tang of the Sound was strong. "Here you are," said Abel. "Just dark enough to hide you and light enough to show the road. Follow that path north, keep on through the pine woods that you'll hit half a mile from here. Then there's a low bluff close by the water, the only house in those parts. Rap on the door and ask for George Millis. Mention John Bolton and Sam Culper."

Grant sprang to the ground. "My thanks to you, Abel. Good night." The chaise rolled off, and Grant struck north along the barely visible path. Forcing himself to a trot, he reached the pine woods, worked on through them. The wind freshened, blew strong, and a heavy rain began to fall. The bluffs could not be far off. All at once he detected the thick, choking reek of wet, charred wood, and sudden fear struck him. He ran on harder through a grayish dawn that rode east on the growing storm. He gave a gasp as he reached the bluffs. There stood a gutted house, its roof gone. In the side yard lay a pig with its throat cut and beyond it a dead cow sprawled. Grant stopped short, shouting, "George! George Millis!" His voice echoed in sinister flatness, was answered only by the drip and patter of the rain falling through the gaping ribs of the roof.

VII

Pursuit

GRANT leaned panting against the blackened door frame. Tragedy
had struck at George Millis, but for the moment, that tragedy
was important only in so far as it affected the news that must be
taken across the Sound. He rallied himself, started off toward the
beach. If he followed it far enough, he would reach the Setuaket
area where Caleb's whaleboats touched. A sudden thought hit him
and he turned inland. Millis's house, he had been told, stood on
the west bank of the Nissequogue River and he would have to
cross that tidal stream before working on east to Setuaket.

The river seemed to trail on endlessly and Grant increased his
pace, helping himself on with the long, silver-headed stick, his
eyes on the slow-brightening sky. In the mists ahead of him, he
heard the scuff of feet, and he ducked into a cluster of bayberry
bushes. Out of the dimness, a Hessian infantryman appeared,
knelt by a little inlet. There was a rattle of oars and the man
pushed a light skiff out into the river, the painter tight in his hand.

Grant leaped forward, flailing out with his stick. He felt it
smack sharply against the man's head, saw him stumble, fall face
down, motionless. Grant pulled him roughly aside, snatched up
the painter, and clambered into the skiff. The current caught the
little craft, pulled at the oars that Grant had snatched up, drove
him on faster and faster. Somewhere ahead he could hear the hiss
of surf. There were sandbanks on either side of him, then there
was no shore at all. The skiff shot forward as though racing down
a flume, lurched, spun, then seemed to whirl under him. The oars
flew from his hands and bitter water poured over the gunwales,

rolled him about, swept him under. He clutched desperately at the splintered side of the skiff, but a wave rushed it away from him, threw an oar just out of reach. He was head down in swirling water, his body twisting and turning. He managed to right himself, was drawn out and out, then at the caprice of the waves, hurtled on toward the beach. The next instant he was in the shallows, struggling against the undertow, working his way foot by foot up the beach. For a moment he knelt, gasping and trying to shake salt water from eyes and ears.

A dry voice said, "Must be wanting to get somewhere pretty bad, mister."

Grant scrambled to his feet, straining through misty eyes at a tall, thin man in rough clothes who was eying him suspiciously. Remembering the Tory reputation of the district, Grant answered curtly. "Any concern of yours? Do you own this beach?"

The man shook his head. "Seems I don't own anything."

Grant looked at him more closely. The beginning of a shallow cut showed under a rough bandage on his forehead and one eye was swollen. His hands were barked and raw and the coarse cloth about his wrists looked charred. Grant made a quick decision. "I'm in a hurry, yes. I want to get to John Bolton as quick as I can, Mr. Millis."

The man's face was impassive. "Bolton? He'd be in the London trade? Or let's put it he's a farmer."

"He's been a lot of things. A schoolteacher, for one."

"So? Yes, guess that's the Bolton I know. How'd you come to name me?"

"Abel Gilman sent me to your house. It was burned. You look as if you'd been in an argument, and there are charred patches on your clothes. You didn't have to be George Millis, but it was an even chance that you might be. I took the chance."

"Yes," said Millis slowly. "You're right. Tory bastards burned me out. So you want to get to Bolton? I'll do what I can, but the weather's making."

"I've got to cross," said Grant stubbornly.

"Mister," said Millis, "you can do two things. You can hire a sea gull to fly you over. Or you can hole up with me till the weather breaks. I've got an old shack back on the dunes. It'll keep out most of the wind and some of the rain. I've got some vittles, and there's salt marsh back of us, so no one's apt to come sniffing at the door. So — yell for a gull or come with me."

The storm, marked by intermittent lashings of rain, held through the whole day and into the night. The following morning saw an end to the rain, but low clouds hung heavy over the Sound and the waves boomed and hissed all along the beach. "What the devil do we do?" fumed Grant.

"Do?" echoed Millis. "We wait."

"Don't you see? That's the one thing I can't do! I'm leaving. It can't be far to Setauket and I'll find — well, I'll find a man I know there."

Millis shook his head. "You're wet and you're torn, and I wouldn't like to watch you trying to explain to curious folk just how you happened to be so."

"You've got too damned much common sense," growled Grant.

The day dragged on under its lowering canopy of cloud. At nightfall Grant and Millis ate a little salt beef and drank tepid, brackish water. Later, Grant fell unexpectedly into a heavy sleep. When he woke the hut was still pitch black, and Millis was snoring in an opposite corner. Grant sat up, listening. The voice of the surf was gone, replaced by a gentle, steady hissing as low waves crisped up the sands.

He stepped out into the night. A few stars showed through ragged clouds. But not far off shore, something flashed red in the night, was followed by a dull, smacking report. Farther to the west red sparks showered to the accompaniment of lighter sounds.

Millis suddenly butted past him, muttering sleepily, "What is it? What's happening?"

There was more fire, more sounds over the dark water. "Look!" yelled Grant. "Whaleboats. You can just make out the hulls."

Millis cried, "That's your gull." He reappeared in a moment with a wad of smouldering tow, lighted at the embers, on the end of a long stick. He waved the stick frantically until the tow burst into smoky yellow flame, then swung the light rhythmically left, left, right and left again.

Scattered shots still flared from the more distant boats, but the nearer was silent and Grant could only catch vague glimpses of it in the musket flares of the other craft. Then it became more distinct and the white flash of oars stood out from the black tide.

Millis flung down his stick and ran to the waterline shouting, "Brewster! Caleb Brewster."

Grant saw Brewster's great bulk vault lightly ashore. Brewster roared, "Millis? I saw the signal. By God, it'd better be important."

"Is," said Millis eloquently, pushing Grant toward the boat.

Brewster's gasp was audible. "Grant! What the hell are you doing here?"

"Never mind," urged Grant. "Get me back to Fairfield quick."

The whaleboat pushed off as Brewster bellowed orders to load the bow gun in its Y mounting. "Wait!" shouted Grant. "George Millis! Get in, for God's sake. We'll take you across."

Millis, a dark shape on the beach, waved a ghostly hand. "Guess not. I'll perhaps be needed here again. Good luck."

Brewster shouted an order, swung the helm over and the whaleboat worked around to the east. "Fairfield it is," he grumbled. "I hate losing a chance to wreck that boatload of Tories, but I'll get you to Tallmadge."

It was close to mid-morning when Grant sprang from the bow of Brewster's whaleboat at Fairfield Beach and headed into town. People stared at his clothes, shrunken by their immersion in sea water, and someone called to him from a fish cart but he only waved in reply.

When he reached the Oxbow he found the porch vacant. As he

hurried up the steps he saw Sergeant Graves just inside the door.
The sergeant came to quick attention when he recognized Grant.

"Morning, sergeant. Where's the major?" asked Grant quickly.

"On patrol, sir, south from the Croton River."

"Oh, blast it!" exclaimed Grant. "Did he leave any orders?"

"That I was to wait for you with two troopers. The old room's
still held for you, sir. Shall I show you to it?"

"Wait a minute. No other orders?" Grant began, but Graves had
already entered the inn and was waiting for Grant to precede him
upstairs.

When they were inside the major's room, Graves unbuttoned his
short jacket and reached inside the lining. He drew out a thin
packet and handed it to Grant. "No need telling the whole street
my jacket was a post office, sir."

With an approving nod, Grant sat down and slipped the cord
from the packet. There were two letters from Laurel, which he
laid aside, turning at once to the official papers. There were routine
orders and copies of orders that told him little beyond the fact
that Colonel Sheldon was on court-martial duty at Old Salem, the
regiment being commanded ad interim by Lieutenant-Colonel John
Jameson, a Virginian, stationed at Northcastle. The last paper was
a single sheet with the inscription "B. T. to G. L." Inside were
a few hasty lines. "On your return to Fairfield, you will remain there until further orders from me. Be alert for anything
from C."

Grant glanced up at Graves. "Nothing later than this?"

"Nothing, sir."

Grant got up and looked out of the window, barely aware of the
sunlit street below. He had planned, in the event of the major's
absence, to strike out immediately into Westchester, being sure
that he would be able to pick up his trail. But the major's message
was uncompromising. And Tallmadge knew where Grant had
been, knew that he might have found out vital secrets. "So," reasoned Grant, "he must feel that my presence here is more important

than my news." He turned to the waiting sergeant. "You and your men are ready to start?"

"Any time, sir."

"Good. Now listen to this carefully. You're to take your men and push on to the post at Green Farms. There you'll pick up Sergeant Turner and one of his men. With them you'll go on to the Stamford post and take two of the troopers there. That'll give you a total of seven sabers, enough to put up a fight if you have to, but not enough to attract much attention. Is that clear?"

"Perfectly, sir."

"Then you'll all head straight into Westchester and keep on going until you find the major. It shouldn't be too hard to pick up his trace."

Grant stepped to the cupboard and found an inkpot, quills and paper. "Here you are, sergeant," he said. "We'll make four copies. You and Turner will have one each. Give the others to those troopers you and he think are most reliable. Ready?"

He began to write slowly, reading aloud each word as it appeared under his pen. Across the table, Sergeant Graves wrote laboriously. The barest frame of what Grant had learned would be enough for Tallmadge. Some coup, probably involving treachery, was on foot against West Point. Very few in British official circles knew the details, but large numbers of troops were being held ready for some move. There was no accumulation of shipping in the Sound, so the move must be up the Hudson. When Grant had reached this point, he sat back and re-read what he had written. Then he added, still speaking slowly, "Most of the above I learned from John Anderson in person."

When Graves and his troopers had clattered out of town, Grant sat frowning at the sheets of unused paper that littered the table. Should he have used André's name? And was he being remiss in not sending an express direct to Arnold, telling him what was known about the threat to West Point? The first point he finally ruled out. The actual identity of John Anderson would be of no immediate use. But the second point nagged at him. He finally made up his mind to conscript, if possible, the first of Caleb Brewster's men who might come into town, mount him somehow and send him to Arnold. He would go out at once to find someone to ride to West Point.

His eyes caught the white glint of Laurel's letters. A smile showed on his face as he began the first, words and phrases standing out from the sheet as he skimmed over it:

DEAR SIR,

I have had the pleasure of your letters about the distressed inhabitants . . . along with the Macys and the Plummers, so they, at least, may face the future more surely . . . a doll or two and a wooden horse were sent to the Jonas children and a plow has been found for the father . . . would value an opportunity to consult with you . . . much good to be done . . . I send this by the post, and shall be happy to see you, but far happier should you give over your present course . . .

He turned to the second:

SIR,

Two nights ago your men burned out the Hilton family. The old grandmother is dead of the shock. Husband and wife are badly injured, but it is thought that they may live. This is a valorous chapter in your fight for what you call freedom!

There was no need to look back to the first letter, so thoroughly cancelled by the second. Grant sat slumped in his chair, fingers drumming nervously on the table. With a sudden gesture he swept the two sheets into a table drawer. Then he got to his feet and tore off his shrunken, sea-stained clothes. "I can't be bothered," he muttered. "I have work to do."

He got into his uniform quickly, clapped on his helmet, and running down to the stable yard, mounted his horse and rode off to Black Rock. There were several whaleboats tied up by the middle wharf and he had no difficulty in making out Brewster's huge form among the men. Grant, dismounting, hailed him. "Look here, Caleb, can you leave post to go inland for a day or two?"

"Not unless it's important enough to spring a leak in the bilges of hell."

"This is. Can you ride?"

"Can, but don't like it much," said Brewster, scratching his chin with a huge thumb.

"Guess you'll have to like it. I've got strict orders from Tallmadge to stay here, or I'd go myself."

"Just tell me where, when and why, and I'll start," said Brewster. "First off though, I've brought a letter for Tallmadge. Better look at it first."

He handed Grant a letter addressed in Culper's neat script to John Bolton, Esquire, c/o Abraham Woodhull. Grant took it, saying, "But it'll be in code and only Tallmadge has the key." When he opened it, he saw the letter was not coded, a sure sign that Culper had written in great haste. He began to read:

MY DEAR FRIEND,

We all arrived here after a passage of two hours. The kindness of yourself & wife & the pleasure I found at yr. house are strongly fixed on my mind & make me desirous of contributing to the information & amusement of you & yrs.

Yr. concern about matters touching commerce and the information you furnished are firm in mind. I confess myself uneasy about the strongboxes at the store, a point or two west of us, but hold it to be most unwise to say aught of the matter to that storekeeper. I propose to treat the matter more fully when next I see you. My respects to the Wistar family & yrs. I shall send the nickanees and the vinny by Tommy. Yrs. affect'ly,

S. CULPER

Grant re-read the letter, trying to translate it in light of other messages received and his own knowledge of the subject matter. The meaning leapt out at him. The store was West Point. The strongboxes, "The forts, by God, the forts," thought Grant. He frowned as he read on.

"Something you don't like much?" inquired Brewster.

"Plenty," Grant muttered, his eyes on the words, "but hold it to be most unwise to say aught of this matter to the storekeeper," which could only mean to Major General Benedict Arnold. "Caleb," he said, "you've known our friend here a long time?"

"Ample," replied Brewster.

"Well, if you thought it absolutely necessary to do something and he said the exact opposite, what would you do?"

"He's saying the opposite pretty strong?"

"Very," said Grant.

"Then," said Brewster, "I'd do as he says. He's always been right. Now about getting me inland."

Grant shook his head. "Our friend says no. So you stay with your lobster fleet. I'll be at the Oxbow as usual, till Tallmadge sends for me. Come over tonight, and we'll break a bottle of Nangle's West India." He started to mount, then with his left foot still in the stirrup, he asked, "By the way, do you know of any Hiltons about here?"

"You must mean Ezra Hilton. Lives a mile down the Stratfield road."

"Is he a Tory?"

"Ezra?" asked Brewster. "I wouldn't say that. But he's the most left-handed, cantankerous curmudgeon that ever broke sod along the Sound. If he brings up a pot jammed with prime lobster, he'll cuss because they aren't crabs. Put him down in a hot Tory section and he'd paint the whole Declaration of Independence across the front of his house. Why?"

"Our people burned him out."

"Burned out Ezra? I'm not surprised. I've heard his cantankerousness led him to set guiding lights on the beach when Tryon burned Fairfield last year. Not that he favored the Crown, but because the folks about him disfavored it. See you tonight."

Grant rode up the long tongue of land and onto the main road. So wrong headedness, not treachery, had led to the Hilton tragedy. What did it matter? The deed was done, and he pushed the whole affair to the back of his mind and turned his thoughts to Culper's letter, which he carefully shredded as he rode along.

There was pasture land sloping northward beyond the road and he put his mare over the low stone wall, heading for a hillock that pushed up a rounded crest well this side of Greenfield Hill. From there he could watch the town and its approaches while he puzzled over Rob Townsend's news and advice.

He heard hoofs on the turf behind him and turned to see Rosa Hollis cantering toward him, waving and laughing. She slowed her horse beside Grant's. "You certainly manage to be in a great many places in very little time, Captain," she said mischievously.

Hand to his helmet, he answered, "Cavalry is supposed to be mobile, Miss Hollis."

"On land *and* sea?"

"How do you mean?"

She flicked her reins impatiently. "Will you never stop fencing? I've heard you made a voyage not long ago, and now I see you managed to get back in time to settle accounts with Ezra Hilton."

"I only heard of the Hiltons today," exclaimed Grant.

Rosa sniffed. "Mish-mash! I suppose you've got to say so. Don't think that *I* care. He is the most disagreeable man in Fairfield County."

"I heard that people were hurt — that there were deaths."

"The grandmother had died hours before you and your men came. The children are safe, since your men thoughtfully chased them into the woods back of the house just to get them out of the way.

"How do you know all this?" Grant asked.

"I've just come from there. When Laurel started down from the Aspetuck with Aunt Ann and some food and blankets and a lot of kickshaws, I went along. The family is living in an old shed that didn't happen to catch fire."

Grant pulled up his mount. "Laurel's over there? How far is it?"

"A world and a half away for you, Captain. You see, it wasn't until Laurel talked with old Ezra that she knew you were in command and saw to the burning."

Grant turned angrily to her. "I've told you I wasn't near the place."

Rosa gave him an odd, twisted smile. "Where were you then?"

A sudden panic came over Grant. Rosa, somehow, seemed to know he had been away on a secret mission. Where could she have picked up the rumor?

Rosa edged her horse closer. "Tell me," she smiled, "isn't it rather fun to swoop down out of the night with your men and surprise a lot of Tories?"

He looked at the roofs of Fairfield to the southwest. Any orders, if the usual courier schedule were followed, could hardly come in before another hour or more. He said abruptly, "I'm going to the Hiltons'. You'll excuse me?"

"Oh ho!" cried Rosa. "So you do know the way. And I certainly won't excuse you. I found a short cut over the fields. Come on. I'll show you." She started off across the pasture, Grant following. At the far end, Grant smelled again the unwholesome tang of charred wood, and saw, beyond some maples, a blackened chimney, a cellarhole choked with burned timbers. Near it stood a flimsy shed, its wide door masked by a sheet of canvas and horses tethered at its far end. "Doesn't it look attractive?" Rosa asked.

The canvas stirred and Laurel emerged, swathed in a white apron and carrying a basin of eggshells which she threw into a hole at the corner of the shed. She moved with a sort of grim purpose, Grant thought, her face set and thoughtful, yet she didn't look particularly angry or disturbed. Then as she turned, she caught sight of Grant and Rosa and her expression changed at once, and he read cold, implacable anger in it. For a moment her eyes were on Grant. Then she vanished back of the canvas without any further sign of recognition. Rosa laughed mockingly, shook her bridle and was gone.

Grant hesitated, then rode up to the shed, dismounted and ducked under the crude curtain. Rough cots had been set up along the wall and from the nearest, a thin man, his head swathed in bandages, glared at him. By the foot of the cot, a little girl whimpered while another pressed close to the man, staring vacantly. Laurel was bent over a woman, arranging a poultice about a swollen throat.

Grant spoke in a low voice. "Laurel! I must talk to you."

Without looking around, she said, "I'm busy. These people are badly off, and you know why. Now go!"

"Then I'll wait outside. But you've got to talk to me."

"I see no reason." Her voice changed as she spoke to Mrs. Hilton. "There. Is that easier?"

"I'll wait," said Grant as he brushed past the canvas into the open air. He paced up and down beside his horse. Why were Laurel and Rosa so sure that he and his men were concerned in this tragedy?

The canvas rustled and Laurel appeared, pale but composed. "I hoped that you wouldn't wait, Captain," she said evenly. "I just came out to gather more herbs." She started past him.

Grant joined her. "Then I'll help you. But I want you to know that my men had nothing to do with this."

"They were identified."

"They couldn't have been. I know where every trooper in Fairfield county is. There aren't enough of them to storm a hen coop. And when this happened, Laurel, I was miles away from here."

"Do you have to say that?" asked Laurel, eyes on the ground. "Mr. Hilton recognized you."

"That's impossible. Come, let's face him now." He suddenly pulled back the canvas and motioned Laurel inside.

A little to his surprise, Laurel stepped in ahead of him and walked to Mr. Hilton's cot. The little girls crowded fearfully toward the head. Grant touched his helmet. "Mr. Hilton, if any of our people were responsible for this, I'll take the matter straight to headquarters. Will you give me a full statement of just what happened?

Laurel bent over the cot. "Mr. Hilton, Captain Ledyard says he wasn't concerned in this — couldn't have been." Her voice was controlled, gently persuasive.

Hilton looked up from his bandages and a bony finger stirred, pointed, "That's him."

Laurel turned quickly, the canvas rustled, and she was gone.

Grant darted after her. "Laurel! Laurel! There's something wrong here, very wrong. I was — I was — confound it, I can't tell you where I was but it wasn't here nor near here. You trusted me before. Can't you now? There's nothing more that I can say except that this was not my work nor our work."

Laurel's glance wavered, changed from cold to deep sadness. "But why is Mr. Hilton so sure about you?"

"I said before, I don't care, but if you want a reason it is probably because he's cantankerous. He wants to think our people are responsible for his suffering. Because I'm in the uniform of my country, he blames me. God knows he's wrong!"

Unexpectedly Laurel said, "I believe you." Her face was grave. "I'm glad that you had nothing to do with this — " her hand indicated the charred cellarhole. "I believe you hate it as much as I do."

"More, perhaps, because I've seen more of it," answered Grant. "I make war against armed men. But people like these," he went on, "they're out of it, so far as I'm concerned, so far as most of the men in the army are concerned. Now when do you go back to the Aspetuck?"

"Soon, I think. Aunt Ann will be back here tonight, and then we'll both go home if the Hiltons are well enough to be left alone."

145

She sighed. "You see, none of their neighbors will do anything for them because the Hiltons believe in the king."

"We'll find a way around that," Grant assured her. "I'll talk to the head of the Fairfield committee. Then we'll see what else can be done. Laurel, I'm going back to Fairfield now. When I have leave, I shall come to see you." When she said nothing, he touched the visor of his helmet and rode off across the fields. As he reached the turn by the white birches, he looked back. Laurel still stood by the shed, watching him. Then she spun about and vanished behind the canvas.

Grant returned to the Oxbow, puzzling over what he had heard at the Hiltons'. He stabled his horse, ordered food sent to his room and ate alone, eyes thoughtful. As he finished his meal, steps pounded on the stairs and Caleb Brewster burst in, flushed and panting.

"A produce boat put in from across the Sound just now," Brewster blurted out. "I didn't know the man in charge, but he said that John Bolton would want this." He tugged at his pocket and produced a huge key. "Mean anything to you?"

Grant got a magnifying glass from the cupboard and studied the key, hoping to find some word or symbol scratched on it. At length he shook his head. "Nothing here."

Brewster helped himself to the rum on Grant's tray. "Must be something," he said. Grant leaned his elbows on the table, slowly twisting the shaft of the key between his fingers. Then he stopped, staring. The key had come apart in his hands, bright metal showing where threads had been cut allowing one section to be screwed into the other. The upper half, some three inches long, was hollow and there was a glint of white in the interior.

With shaking fingers, Grant prodded gingerly at the opening while Brewster cried, "Look out! You'll tear it. Take a quill — no, the end of those dividers. Easy! It's beginning to rip!"

At last a fragile paper cylinder lay on the table. Grant flattened it out while Brewster shoved a sheet of foolscap under it. "See anything?" breathed Brewster.

"It's not from New York. Wrong handwriting." Grant's voice dropped to a whisper. "Listen!"

> Verbal from Culper. J. A. has been in correspondence for a long time with an American officer who signs himself either as "Gustavus" or "Mr. Moore." Said officer believed to be still in service and to hold important command. WOODHULL.

Grant felt a sensation of sickly cold in the pit of his stomach. By word of mouth from Robert Townsend to Austin Roe to Abraham Woodhull the message had come, then across the Sound in writing. This clumsy iron key was perhaps the key to the real meaning of what he had learned at Raynham Hall. John Anderson — or John André — had been able to find a willing correspondent of some rank within the American lines, call him Gustavus or Mr. Moore. As a result of that correspondence some coup was afoot for a bloodless conquest of the vital West Point forts. And the Commander, at this crucial moment, was in faraway Hartford, conferring with Rochambeau.

Brewster's voice made him start. "Damn it, Grant, I asked you what it meant!"

With a feeling of physical numbness, Grant wearily sketched out for him the news from Raynham Hall. Brewster went pale under his sea tan.

"What do we do?" he asked huskily.

"What we talked of over at Black Rock. Get word to Tallmadge. He knows everything except what we've just had. I'll — here, give me that key and the tissue." Grant wrote carefully along a sheet of foolscap:

> The threat specifically concerns the West Point forts. Culper *urges* that no word be sent on to commander of those forts. Further data on enclosed tissue. N. B. I should have reported earlier that J. A. may be John André, adjutant general to Sir H. C.

He dried the writing, ripped off the foolscap, rolled the tissue up in it and inserted the papers into the hollow shaft of the key. "There you are, Caleb. Give that to the trooper at Green Farms and he'll pass it on to Tallmadge. Show your man how it works."

"Is that safe?"

"These troopers are all picked men. Tallmadge will get it. You get a horse from Moobie. I'll send word to your senior sergeant that you'll be gone for awhile."

After Brewster had gone, concern etched deep lines on either side of Grant's mouth. If more messages came he now had no messenger to send out until Caleb's return. Ten miles and more. It would take a good two hours, since Caleb was not the best of riders, and would have to spend some time explaining matters to the Green Farms trooper. He got up, walked out to the end of the Green, head bowed and hands behind his back. He turned abruptly as he heard the rumble of wheels crossing the Black Rock bridge. A chaise rolled into sight, and he could make out Laurel driving it, a weedy-looking boy by her side. She drove straight on, her head moving from side to side as though looking for some particular house or sign. "Probably after medicines or supplies," thought Grant. "At any rate, I'll get a word with her."

He started toward the oncoming chaise at a brisk walk, then stopped, the chaise forgotten. Hoofs were drumming in from the west, from the direction that Brewster had taken. Grant spun about, raced toward the Oxbow just as a single rider, jaunty in blue and red, pulled up by the porch. "What's happened?" panted Grant. "Where's Brewster?"

The rider dropped to the ground. "Who's Brewster? I've got — well, if it isn't Grant Ledyard! Where the devil did you drop from? I thought you'd gone south with Benny Lincoln."

Grant recognized Cornelis Verplanck of the New York Line, with whom he had done patrol work along the Schuylkill and the Delaware. Disregarding the questions, he said sharply, "Did Tallmadge send you?"

"Send me? No, I'm looking for him."

"He's in Westchester."

Verplanck tugged a packet out of his saddlebags. "Then can you take this damned thing off my hands?" He peeled off a letter and gave it to him. "Sign here."

As Grant signed, he glanced down the road. The chaise was halted before a partially rebuilt house. The front seat was empty, and the weedy boy stood by the horse's head. Then Grant handed the receipt back to Verplanck, eyebrows rising as he noted the writing on the cover of the letter. "So you're at West Point. Is this urgent?"

"Just routine. Yes, I've been at the Point since Arnold took command. Dick Varick and Dave Franks are with me. Things are quiet. Mrs. Arnold's come up state with the baby."

"Mrs. Arnold? The general must feel pretty sure of things up there," commented Grant.

"Why not? We're a million miles from the war. It's all calm as Haverstraw Bay in the dog days. Arnold's sent a whole lot of Massachusetts infantry upriver to cut firewood and a big bunch inland on the same detail, so I guess the garrison'll keep warm this winter. When I left, the engineers were getting ready to pull up the barrier chain that stretches across the Hudson below the forts. Just a repair job, but I'm glad I'm out of it."

"Hauling up the chain that blocks the channel! Isn't that risky?"

"I don't think so. We'd have plenty of warning if a flotilla left New York to come up river. There's no sign of that. Of course, they have had an armed sloop, the *Vulture,* lying off Teller's Point by the mouth of Croton River, but that doesn't mean anything."

"N — no," said Grant slowly. "I suppose not." With an effort he pushed away depression and apprehension. He noted Verplanck's travel-stained uniform and dusty boots. "Come in and have some rum and tell me more about the Point. Who else is up there with you?"

Verplanck shook his head ruefully. "Can't take the time. I've

149

got to push on to New Haven and God knows what hour I'll be there." He mounted stiffly and clattered off with a wave of farewell.

Grant stood watching him, flicking the routine message from West Point against his cuffs. Far down the street he could still see Laurel's chaise. Opening the letter as he went, Grant started down the street. The seals gave way and he automatically checked his gait.

The first paragraph was in Arnold's recent fulsome vein, extolling the virtues of one Benjamin Tallmadge. The next — the script stood out boldly from the paper:

> . . . If a Mr. James Anderson, a person I expect from New York, should arrive at your quarters, I have to request that you will give him an escort of two horse to bring him on his way to this place, and send an express to me that I may meet him. If your business will permit, I wish you to come with him.

Slowly he turned and began walking back to the Oxbow. He noticed the date on the letter, September 19, 1780. "Damned funny. This is the twenty-second. What took so long?" Then he remembered that Washington had crossed the Hudson on the eighteenth with his suite to begin his journey to Hartford. Arnold and his staff would have acted as ceremonial escort. There would have been salutes from the batteries on both sides and probably an inspection of troops under Arnold's immediate command. All that would have held up paper work so perhaps the delay was not surprising. And Grant told himself that James Anderson was *not* John Anderson — couldn't be.

But a man might be John Anderson on one side of the Sound and James on the other. Or "James" might have been a slip of the pen for security reasons. A trap? Arnold was eager to be in touch with all secret agents in the area, and if this anxiety became known to Sir Henry Clinton, might not the latter, through false spies, arrange an ambush into which Arnold could fall? Reason prompted,

"Arnold's no fool. And besides the letter says 'James.'" Grant thought of the warnings of Culper, particularly the latest; the talks that he and Polly Morgan had heard at Oyster Bay; the British and Hessian troops standing by on Long Island, waiting; the great bodies of Massachusetts infantry sent up river and inland, far from the forts, in search of firewood; the great barrier chain taken up for repairs.

He gave a sudden shake to his head. There was no choice. Tallmadge's orders to remain at Fairfield would have to be broken. A few moments later, mounted and armed, he rode out of the Oxbow yard at a gallop, hens, dogs and cats scurrying from his path, his route forming in his mind. First he would intercept Brewster on the latter's return from Green Farms. Then he must strike northwest, heading for Northcastle, the headquarters of the regiment, hoping to cross Tallmadge's path somewhere en route.

The western sun was low. A brisk wind whipped the trailing white plume of Grant's helmet about the back of his neck in an irritating rasp and tickle. He brushed at it mechanically. James Anderson and John Anderson. Gustavus and Mr. Moore. The scattered garrison at West Point. The huge barrier chain dragged up from the Hudson.

"Where the devil do you think you're going?" The sudden shouted challenge brought Grant abruptly from his reverie. He saw Caleb Brewster coming toward him through the sunset glow.

Grant reined-in impatiently beside Brewster. "Can't stop to explain. A courier came through from West Point with a dispatch. It's got to go on to Tallmadge."

Brewster stared at him. "You had orders from the major not to leave Fairfield without his instructions, and when Ben Tallmadge says stay, he means stay."

"I know the orders," Grant said soberly. "But this time I've got to break them. This is urgent. Remember what Culper wrote about Anderson? Arnold expects a visitor from New York by that name. When Anderson comes through Fairfield, we're ordered to hurry him on to Arnold. Also the West Point garrison's been scattered and the barrier chains are to be pulled out of the Hudson."

Brewster's eyes narrowed until they were only bright slits in his face. He wrenched his horse about awkwardly. "Get going, Grant. You've got to."

When Grant cleared the ruins of Green Farms he followed a winding road that slanted northwest away from the Sound and led into an endless stretch of steep, tree-clad hills and deep valleys where the night shadows were beginning to gather. On and on he rode. At midnight he reckoned he was well into New York State. By a swift brook that poured silver down a black rock, he watered his horse, adjusted girth and bridle while he listened to the night wind. He distrusted the unfathomable silence. He was unable to shake off a growing impression that he was not alone among the dark hills, that other men were moving along the sandy roads under the pines.

With an impatient shake of his helmet, Grant mounted. "Getting jumpy as an upcountry recruit!" he thought irritably. "The night's dead calm. I could hear a woodchuck cleaning his whiskers two counties away." He pushed on at a quick pace, orienting himself as well as he could by the stars.

At the end of a mile or two he turned his horse into the shadow of a cart path that led off the road. Ahead of him, growing steadily louder, he could hear the slow thump of hoofs, the thin jingle of equipment. The sound came nearer, and he made out several helmeted heads against the star-studded sky. Silver helmets, not the ominous brass of the British. He called, "Who goes there?"

A brisk voice answered, "Patrol. 1st Company, 2nd Dragoons. Who are you?"

Grant reined in by a corporal, a tall man whose legs dangled on either side of a most inadequate horse. "Captain Ledyard of the same. Attached to Major Tallmadge. Have you seen the major tonight?"

The corporal shook his head. "Heard he's ranging the south, but we ain't seen him."

"Can you spare me a couple of men from your squad?"

"Under orders, sir," said the corporal. "Strict. We're to patrol to the Fairfield line and wait there for a squad from the 3rd, coming in from the north."

"Not just one man?" urged Grant, eying the other troopers who were lolling in their saddles, apparently glad of the halt.

"Show me authority and you can take the whole squad, sir. Otherwise — " he left his sentence trailing in the air.

"Quite right," Grant admitted reluctantly. "Look here, I've got to find the major. How would you head if you wanted to pick up his trail? What would you do?"

The corporal scratched his head. "I'd ask questions, same as you, sir. Now there's plenty roads the major could take, leading up from the White Plains section, and you'd never be able to scout 'em all in a night. But if the major's trending into Northcastle from the south, he's pretty near bound to hit the road up from Tarrytown and then follow it in. There's a hill five miles out of Northcastle, and I'd tether my horse there and wait till the major appeared down on the road. Then I'd holler to him."

Grant flicked his reins impatiently. "If that's the best I can do, it's the best I can do."

"If you're so minded, take this road straight on till you come to a pond on the left — " he continued his instructions while Grant listened attentively.

"I think I have it now, corporal. When I come to the burned mill I take the right road and that'll run me into the Tarrytown road."

"And the hill's a mile west down it. Good night, sir, and good luck."

"Good luck and thank you," answered Grant and trotted off.

Through the morning hours, Grant waited on the hill above the Tarrytown road. Occasional carts rolled down the highway below him, their dust rising into the clear September air, but except for them, the roads and fields lay empty and silent. At ten o'clock, Grant considered saddling up his horse and riding south in the hope of coming on Tallmadge and his men and putting an end to the interminable waiting. He walked slowly toward his grazing horse, still irresolute.

There was metal gleaming down on the road, the dull sheen of a musket barrel. Grant drew his pistols, made his way quickly but silently down the slope. A tall, bareheaded man was ambling along in the direction of Northcastle, pitted musket slung over his back. He wore a green Hessian coat with faded red facings. Grant glided onto the road, pistols leveled. "Hands up!" he snapped.

The man flung his arms high above his head. "Sure, if it pleasures you, mister," said the man.

"Who are you?" asked Grant quickly.

"John Paulding, mister. Farm near Tarrytown."

"What's your party?"

"The Upper party. What you think?"

Pistols still level, Grant said, "Got anything to show it?"

"Not with my hands like this."

"A paper?" asked Grant, watching him carefully. "Get it out with one hand. Toss it onto the road."

With wonderful contortions of a long arm, Paulding extracted a soiled paper from his coat and dropped it. Grant picked it up and over the signature of Lieutenant Colonel Jameson read that John Paulding was a duly enrolled member of the volunteer militia. A brief and unmistakable description of the bearer followed. Grant nodded. "That's all right. Drop your arms. What are you doing in a Hessian coat?"

Paulding looked sadly at him. "I wear what I can find."

"Where have you been?"

"Lot of us have been ranging up the hills these last two nights. The Commander's due back from Hartford any day now. We didn't want no mishaps to him."

"Many of you?"

"I'd say every able-bodied man from here to the Fairfield line. Mister, these hills has been busting with us."

"Under orders?"

"Unofficial as hell."

Grant remembered his feeling during the night that men were moving about him, never close, never seen nor heard, a feeling that had persisted in his mind. An unofficial guard of honor for the Commander. He addressed Paulding again. "Did you come across any of our cavalry?"

Paulding shook his head. "The boys said that Benny Tallmadge was out with his iron heads, but I ain't seen 'em."

"If Tallmadge were heading for Northcastle, he'd have to pass along here, wouldn't he?"

"He'd sort of have to, unless he'd struck in way east of here, and that ain't likely," answered Paulding.

"Want to take a scout south for me and see if you find him?"

"Can't hardly," said Paulding. "I'm Northcastle-bound. I got a prisoner to give Jameson there."

Grant stared at him. "You've got a prisoner? For God's sake where?"

Paulding jerked a grimy thumb. "Down the road a piece. Ike van Wart and Dave Williams have got him. Seems his feet hurt, and they stopped to let him dabble 'em in a brook."

"What is he? British or Hessian?"

"Don't rightly know, but mister, has he got pretty clothes! Blue overcoat, claret undercoat. Kind of elegant."

"A civilian? Are you sure you've got the right to hold him?"

"Ample right, mister. With his own breath he told us he held to the Lower party."

"What's his name?"

"Oh, that's all right, too. It's writ out pretty. The name's John Anderson."

"I see," said Grant slowly. "John Anderson. Of course." His

palms were suddenly moist, and he was conscious of his heart beating rapidly.

"Know him?" asked Paulding in mild surprise.

"I've heard the name," answered Grant, his mind still repeating 'Anderson' over and over. John or James, what difference did it make?

"Look here," said Grant, "You say you're taking him to North-castle? I'll ride on with you. I'll see that you turn your man over to Jameson and get credit for him. My horse is up the hill. I'll bring him down here." He ran up the slope while Paulding sat patiently on a boulder, waiting for his comrades and the prisoner.

Under the pines, Grant adjusted his bridle, tightened the girth and led his mount downward, weaving carefully between tree trunks and boulders. Through the interlaced branches he caught glimpses of the road below him. He was close enough to hear the crunch of boots. A few more steps and he would be face to face with John Anderson, would know for *sure* who John Anderson was.

He gave a wrench to his bridle, dragged his horse out of the last bushes. Pauling was talking with two well set up countrymen, one of whom led a riderless horse. Between them stood a man in a claret-colored coat, a long blue overcoat across one arm, a small, slim man with carefully dressed hair.

The group shifted and Grant saw the man in the claret-colored coat. Major John André, adjutant general to Sir Henry Clinton, looked calmly about him, then his eyes fell on Grant. There was a quick flicker of recognition in the major's expression. Then it was carefully masked.

Grant said, "Good evening, Major. Our positions seem to be changed since our last meeting."

André's laugh seemed utterly natural. "Good evening, Captain. I'm greatly flattered at your giving me military rank. My name is — "

"I know," said Grant. "John Anderson."

A light shadow came over André's face. Then he laughed again. "Of course. These men here must have told you."

"Just where had you been when they halted you?"

"I?" André gave a careless gesture. "Walking for my health. It's something my physician recommends."

"In what direction?"

"Oh, as to that," André began airily. "I was — but look here. This is a damned uncomfortable place to stand quizzing. These young friends of mine had talked of taking me on to Colonel Jameson. I hope you won't think me rude if I suggest that further questioning be postponed until we are in his presence."

"I can hardly force you to talk against your will," said Grant.

André smiled engagingly. "I knew you'd be reasonable about it." He glanced at his captors. "Now, let's get on to Northcastle."

Grant mounted reluctantly and the little group set off through the cool, sunny afternoon. Paulding, van Wart and Williams plodded along, dogged and workmanlike. Their prisoner, still tethered to his horse, walked among them with a light, dancer's step. His head was high, and he kept looking to right and left as though enjoying a pleasant outing. A dozen yards in the rear, Grant watched the four with an uneasy eye. But those men would never let André slip through their fingers. They wanted credit at headquarters for his capture as well as the reward that would come to them from André's valuables, theirs under law. Other militiamen joined Paulding and his friends, and formed a sort of escort for them.

When from a low rise the scattered houses of Northcastle appeared, Grant felt a deep sense of relief. Bright-helmeted troopers moved briskly about a white farmhouse standing in a field. Others were gathering at a shed that jutted out from a low yellow house in a hollow, and Grant could make out the pale flicker of flame under slung camp kettles. "Jameson's quarters," thought Grant. John Anderson would be turned over to Jameson. He stirred impatiently in the saddle, eager to begin the questioning. The colonel, of course, would conduct matters, but no one in the American

Army, except perhaps Tallmadge, could guide that questioning better than Grant. He gathered his reins, ready to ride up and lead the party.

A pleasant-looking man with short, curly hair reached up and caught Grant's bridle. "Don't want to make trouble, Cap, but John Paulding and the others kind of aim to take their prize in alone."

Grant tried to free his reins. "Don't be fools! I've got business with Colonel Jameson. Come on. Let me go."

The smiling man spoke soothingly. "In a little while, Cap. Say maybe a half hour. Easy! We don't want to play rough but if need be, we'll have to rope you up and sit on you. There's six of us. Ain't it better to be reasonable?"

Sudden anger, intensified by the long night ride, flared in Grant's brain. He snatched at his reins. "God damn it, stand clear. I'm going through. Hinder me, and you'll find yourselves standing court-martial on about ten counts."

"Oh, no, Cap." The man's smile broadened. "No soldier law for us. We're volunteer militiamen. No regiment, no officers. Just us." Still holding the reins, he leaned an arm confidentially on the horse's neck. "It's like this, Cap. Been more'n once that the soldier-suit boys have taken prisoners away from us and we don't see a cracked farthing of what's due us by law. I don't say *you'd* do that, but Paulding just wants to feel safe."

Grant said resignedly, "All right. But I know a lot about that prisoner that Jameson's got to hear. Besides, I'm getting hungry."

The man beside him nodded approvingly. "Now that's what I call reasonable, seasonable and feasonable of you, Cap. You won't have to tarry too long. Hey, Lem. You can spare a slice of that cold beef and a little bread from your wallet. Eph Tucker, you give him a pull at that rum bottle we took off'n the old farmer down to Buttermilk Hill."

While the men watched him closely, Grant ate a slice of rare roast beef wedged between two chunks of bread, drank sparingly of the thick, under-aged rum. Between bites, he studied the distant village. Paulding and his men were guiding André to the white farmhouse. He saw the group halted by a mounted guard, then passed on to two men by the door. There was a brief pause, after which they all disappeared into the farmhouse. As he ate, Grant felt increasingly easier. It was just as well to let the preliminary routine questioning go on. He could add nothing to that. Then, with André under secure guard, Grant would have a confidential talk with Jameson after which the major would be held to wait the Commander's pleasure.

He spoke to the nearest guard. "Are you timing this half-hour? Have you got a watch?"

"Sun's good enough for me, Cap. More rum?"

Grant shook his head, his eyes on the farmhouse. What was Jameson saying to John Anderson? It was probable that André would not identify himself, at least for the present. The news of the capture of one suspicious civilian with a very ordinary name would not spread from Northcastle, probably would not reach the ears of the "fairly important American officer" of whom Culper had written, the officer known as Gustavus or Mr. Moore. That gentleman would, for a while at least, feel secure in his treachery.

The man who had stopped Grant peered toward Northcastle. "Guess you can amble any time you got a mind to, Cap," he remarked.

His thoughts interrupted, Grant looked up. There was a stir about the door of the white farmhouse. An orderly appeared, more troopers, followed by Paulding, van Wart and Williams. Then John André stepped easily and confidently into the sunshine, a trooper on either side of him. One of them held a stirrup for him, and he mounted the same horse to which he had been tethered earlier by Paulding. Grant's jaw dropped. "God Almighty! They're letting him go!" he cried.

As though in answer to his words, there was a stir by the picket lines and ten troopers rode up to the house, a junior officer or a sergeant guiding them. The detail formed a double file about André and the leader seemed to be shouting instructions to his men. Another trooper emerged from the doorway, mounted and galloped off, this time taking the road that led north to the Hudson and the high lands about Peekskill. The detail surrounding André milled about, then started off in the wake of the last orderly.

"Where the devil are they taking the prisoner?" shouted Grant.

"Him? Oh, to the red barn. It's a sight stronger than it looks. He won't get free."

Grant barely heard the last words. He touched his mount with his spurs and raced off toward the white house, where he pulled up abruptly. As he dismounted he saw that André and his escort were coming abreast of the barn. An impatient voice from the doorway made him turn. "Something you want, Captain?"

"Captain Ledyard, from Fairfield. I'd like to see Colonel Jameson at once."

The other answered, "I'm Captain Miller, adjutant to the colonel. What do you want to see him about?"

"That prisoner," said Grant quickly. "The man called John Anderson."

Miller shook his head. "The colonel is busy. Maybe he can see you later. From Fairfield, are you?" He began to laugh. "A lot of use you and your crowd are. We've had to send our best men and horses to Tallmadge down there to chase spies. By God, it's good! Then we catch a really big one right up here, someone who must have been running around under your noses all the time!"

Grant started to answer angrily, but checked himself. He said smoothly, "I guess the credit's yours all right, if he really is a spy."

"Ho!" cried Miller, nettled. "You should have seen the papers that I saw, papers that Paulding and his boys found in his stockings.

Grant laughed. The idea that the astute André had incriminating papers on his person was absurd.

Miller began tapping a thin forefinger into his other palm. "Listen to this: *Item No. 1.* There was Major Bauman's report of the ordnance in all the forts and batteries around West Point. *Item No. 2.* A report on the number of men needed to man the works. *Item No. 3.* An account of the weak spots in the defenses. *Item No. 4.* A transcript of a statement about defense made by the Commander at a council of generals. Of course he's a spy." He glared in triumph at Grant, who could only stare dumbfounded.

Miller was enjoying his triumph. "Oh, we've got him all right. And do you know *who* had signed Anderson's pass? Do you know who signed those reports?" He laughed harshly. "No. You don't. Maybe you'll hear some day."

Grant nodded absently while his mind, almost unbidden, began its own process of elimination. Major Bauman? Yes, for the ordnance report. The Frenchman Villefranche? Yes, for the works, but not the guns. General Knox? Hardly. He was concerned with the field guns rather than fortress artillery. Then all at once he knew and the knowledge shook him so deeply that he could feel his shoulders trembling.

Benedict Arnold had sent hundreds of good Massachusetts infantrymen far away from the fort on the pretext of woodcutting. He had ordered the chain lifted from the Hudson — to afford passage to his Majesty's ships. He had asked for the names of men engaged in confidential work. Grant spoke through stiff lips. "I want permission to talk to John Anderson. Now!"

Miller blinked in amazement. "He's not here! God no! He's been sent away, of course."

"I know," Grant's voice cracked. "To the red barn."

"No. To his Excellency General Benedict Arnold and, by God, Arnold will make him sweat, I tell you."

"You — you've sent him to *Arnold?*" Grant took a step backward, then butted past Miller into the house. "Out of my way." He brushed past a gaping orderly and opened the door at the end of the hall. In the bare room a weary looking lieutenant colonel of cavalry was bent over a pile of papers. Grant cried, "Colonel Jameson! Stop him. For God's sake stop him!"

VIII

John Anderson

COLONEL Jameson raised his head and said icily, "Appointments are made through my adjutant. Kindly close the door as you leave."

"Sir, I've seen your adjutant. This matter can't wait. The man Anderson — "

Jameson rose slowly, obviously controlling himself with difficulty. He cleared his throat and Grant saw that his hands were trembling with fatigue. "You'll leave the name of your commanding officer with my adjutant. I shall recommend disciplinary action, most strongly."

Grant cried, "I know this is irregular, sir. As for reporting me, I'm under your own command. Captain Ledyard, attached to Major Tallmadge at Fairfield. I had no business pushing Captain Miller aside and I'll apologize to him. But for God's sake, Colonel, recall the man Anderson."

Jameson reseated himself. "Ledyard. Of course. Sit down, Captain. Didn't mean to storm at you. What about Anderson?"

"Yesterday afternoon, a letter came to Fairfield, asking us to be on the lookout for him," Grant began, as he seated himself.

Jameson shook his head. "Only yesterday? I had one some days ago. So did Colonel Sheldon. The matter is being seen to."

Grant was on his feet again. "That's what I'm afraid of, sir. It's not only that letter. There's so much more. Warnings have come to us, bit by bit, from the other side. We've picked a little ourselves in Fairfield. It builds up into something damnable, something that can be fatal. For God's sake, sir, take my word that trouble's afoot and moving faster and faster that'll blow us, all of us, right off the continent. If you want to save what we believe in, for Heaven's sake call back your troopers and Mr. Anderson!"

Jameson studied Grant carefully and approval came into his weary eyes. "I'm going to commend you in orders, Captain, for strict attention to duty. But don't worry about Mr. Anderson. I'm sending him on to General Arnold. If you know the general as well as I do, you'll stop fretting."

Grant exploded. "That's just it. I'll go over the whole matter with you later but — " his fist beat out the words on the table — "but John Anderson must *not* meet Benedict Arnold."

Jameson frowned dubiously. "The West Point command's just the place for Anderson, just the place where he'll have to answer a lot of damned embarrassing questions. Do you know — " he put his elbows on the table and looked seriously at Grant — "Do you know that the fellow actually had a pass, signed by General Arnold? I'd not want to be in his shoes when he faces Arnold, especially in the general's present temper. Oh, Anderson'll be even safer, from our standpoint, at West Point than here. Now if you'll excuse me, Captain."

Grant's fists clenched in exasperation. "Once again, sir, recall Anderson or — " Voices sounded out in the hall. Spurs clanked and there was a rap on the door. Jameson spoke wearily, "Would you mind opening it, Ledyard?" Grant flung the door open and stepped back, staring at Benjamin Tallmadge who stood erect on the other side of the threshold. Then Tallmadge spoke quickly. "I got your messages from the Green Farms posts. What's happened?"

"Everything, sir. I've been trying to explain to Colonel Jameson — "

Tallmadge, hard faced and unsmiling, laid a hand on Grant's cuff. "I see. Wait right here. I've got to report." He strode into the room, unruffled and courteous and saluted his superior. "Patrol completed, sir. To White Plains and beyond. Nothing significant in the area. Now, sir, with your permission, I'd like to question

Captain Ledyard in your presence." Jameson, still puzzled, nodded assent. Tallmadge turned to Grant. "That identification you wrote about. Your Oyster Bay acquaintance. You're sure?"

Grant felt a great weight lifted from him. "There's not the least doubt. More than that, I saw Anderson within the last hour. He's been sent on to West Point."

Jameson broke in, "Under heavy guard. My orders. He'll be turned over to General Arnold."

"To Gustavus! Or to Mr. Moore! One and the same!" Grant shouted.

"Yes," said Tallmadge slowly. "I've come to that conclusion, too. Brewster forwarded another message from Culper after you'd left Fairfield."

Jameson, his head in his hands, sighed. "Would you gentlemen mind explaining to me just what you're talking about?"

"You've not gone into details, Grant?" asked Tallmadge.

"There's not been time. I've been urging the colonel to recall Anderson."

"Of course," said Tallmadge tersely. "May I ask, Colonel, if you talked with the man Anderson?"

"Certainly," answered Jameson. "He wouldn't say much." He mentioned the pass signed by Arnold in Anderson's name, the reports on the defenses, garrison and armament of the Hudson forts, the résumé of the Commander's conference with his generals.

"And those papers, Colonel?" asked Tallmadge. "May I see them?"

Jameson looked surprised. "The papers? My dear major, I had no right to keep them. I sent them, with a brief account of Anderson's arrest, to the Commander. They'll reach him somewhere this side of the Connecticut line."

"To the Commander?" exclaimed Tallmadge. "Not to Arnold?"

"No. He'd know their contents anyway. But I did send him, by special courier a copy of my letter to the Commander. It has a description of the papers of course."

Tallmadge turned on his heels and walked to the window, chin on his chest. For a moment he stood looking out over the sunlit meadow to the west. Then he faced Jameson. "Excuse me, Colonel, but the matter is of great urgency. Recall Anderson. Above all, recall that courier with the letter to West Point."

Jameson bristled. "Why?"

"Because, sir, if you don't, you'll be compounding the blackest, most damnable bit of treason that's ever touched this continent."

Jameson got to his feet. "Watch your tongue, Major."

Tallmadge went on. "Listen. We've known for a long time that something's been brewing. Most we had from, let us say, a friend outside our lines. I found out a few things. Ledyard, at great personal risk, discovered more. It involves the sale to our enemies of the West Point forts. John Anderson, Colonel, is actually Major John André, adjutant general to Sir Henry Clinton. The captain will confirm that."

Grant nodded. "I met Major André at Oyster Bay, where he got a letter addressed to John Anderson. There's no mistake, Colonel."

"Thanks, Captain," said Tallmadge. "Now Colonel, we also learned that this plan for the treacherous sale of West Point was the result of a dicker between André, acting for Clinton, and an American officer who signed himself as either Gustavus or Mr. Moore."

There was a tragic, stunned look in Jameson's eyes. He seemed to force himself upright in his chair. "No. It's too fantastic. Too utterly damnable. Treason! We've had incompetent fools in high places, we've had vacillation, timidity, but never treason." His voice sank to a dry rustle. "Never!"

"We have it now," said Tallmadge. "What we lack is time. We must have John Anderson here. Bring him back!"

"Suppose you're wrong?" muttered Jameson.

"Then no harm's done," said Tallmadge. "We still have a bona fide prisoner. A few hours to consider his disposition won't do any harm."

"All right," said Jameson reluctantly. He wrote a few lines on a sheet of paper, stepped to the door. "Captain Miller! Have Lieutenant Cox and two troopers overtake the prisoner and his escort and bring them back here."

Grant and Tallmadge exchanged glances. The major said earnestly, "Believe me, sir, you'll never regret this. Did your order include the recall of the courier to General Arnold?"

"No!" Jameson's jaw snapped on the word. "It's my duty to notify my superior officer. I've gone farther than I want in recalling the prisoner."

There was a silence in the room. Grant felt empty and defeated. Then Tallmadge spoke and the tone of his voice shot sudden hope through Grant. The major was saying, "With all due respect, Colonel, is that your final decision?"

"Utter and absolute," answered Jameson.

"In that case, sir," said Tallmadge and there was a serene confidence in his face, "may I withdraw? I'm going to take my troopers, ride on to West Point and — "

"And what?"

"Arrest General Benedict Arnold on charges of high treason!"

Jameson went white as Grant gave an exclamation of joy and hitched at his saber, shouting, "I'm with you, sir."

Jameson's jaw sagged. "Arrest — arrest General *Arnold?*"

"Or Gustavus or Mr. Moore, as you please. They're all the same person. We *know* it. With your permission, sir, I'll leave at once. Ready, Grant?"

Jameson was leaning forward over the table, incredulous. "You can't do that. I certainly won't sanction it."

"You don't have to, sir. I'll take full responsibility. Your name needn't even appear in any later inquiries. Just Ledyard and myself!"

Grant moved toward the door. "I'll warn the troopers, Major."

"You stay where you are," barked Jameson. "Now look here, Major. I've got respect for your judgment and integrity. But I can't

166

permit this. General Arnold's my superior. How'll I look if you've made a mistake? Men of my regiment arresting a full major general. Oh, no!"

"As I said, Colonel, officially you'll know nothing about this." Jameson said firmly, "Give over this plan of yours, Tallmadge. If you don't give me your word you'll make no such attempt — I'd hate to have to put you under arrest, but I'd have to."

Grant, his hand on the latch of the door, watched Tallmadge. The major seemed to freeze and all expression left his face. He said, "You leave me no choice, Colonel. I'll not make the attempt." He glanced toward Grant whose hand was still on the latch. "Don't press the matter, Grant. We'll just have to pray that American luck will hold for us, somehow."

Jameson struck his hands together in approval. "Now that's being sensible, both of you. Ready to talk about the posts and the horses, Major? Then pull up a chair. Glad to have the chance of meeting you, Captain Ledyard."

Grant took a last look at Tallmadge, but the major had drawn up to the table apparently absorbed in thoughts of the coming discussion. Grant touched the brim of his helmet and left the room. Without knowing just where he was going, he walked dully out across the meadows.

Chewing a blade of grass, he tried to rally from the shock of the colonel's refusal either to intercept the messenger to Arnold or to allow Tallmadge to ride to the Hudson with his troopers. Time was slipping away. The prisoner had been recalled, but two couriers were riding out the sun, one to the east and one to the west. Of course, if the east-bound rider met the Commander returning from Hartford, the situation might be saved. But supposing the Commander did not follow the southern route. Supposing he stopped to inspect depots. "We're counting on luck and nothing else," he thought.

Troopers were leading their horses to water at a brook that wandered through the field. Almost unconsciously he recognized the bandy-legged stride of the officer in charge of the group. It was Lieutenant Gunnison. The troopers with him must be Tallmadge's patrol. Picked men, of course, some of the best in the regiment. Good man, Gunnison, by Tallmadge's accounts. Ready for any kind of service, resourceful. "I'm senior to Gunnison," thought Grant. Slowly he rose from the stone wall and began walking, uncertainly at first, then with gathering speed. He broke into a trot, calling, "Gunnison!"

Gunnison recognized him. "Hello, Captain. What are you brewing now?"

"Let your sergeant see to the watering. Come over here out of earshot. Are your men fresh?"

Gunnison raised his eyebrows. "Had quite a ride with Major Ben. But they're middling."

"You in command in the major's absence?"

Gunnison laughed. "Sure I am."

"Then listen to me. Get through your watering quickly then mount up your men. No bugles, no noise. You've got to take me on faith. Take your detail west, heading for the ground above Peekskill. Don't pass that white house where Jameson is. I'll ride with you, at the head of the column, with one of your troopers for a guide."

Gunnison still looked troubled. "Is this something Tallmadge wants done?" he asked.

Grant hesitated. "He — yes. He wants it done. You take my word that he wants it. We've got big stakes, Gunnison. We're going to arrest a general."

Gunnison brightened. "What? Arrest a general? Fine! Never done that before. Which one?"

Grant stepped still closer and dropped his voice. "Arnold."

Gunnison's eyes bulged. "Arnold?" Then he made flipping motions with his hands. "Pick up the cards. You're dealing a game I don't know."

Grant spoke with earnestness. "This has got to be done. If you want to back out, all right. In that case, I'll relieve you from command and take your detail. But the detail's going and I'm going."

Gunnison dug his spur into the ground. "God Almighty! I might as well come along. Going to tell me anything more?"

"Better not. I'll be in command, and the troopers mustn't know a thing. All that matters to them is that they're riding to Arnold's headquarters at the Robinson house."

"Here we go," groaned Gunnison. "I'll pass the word along, quietly. The boys are used to this sort of thing."

"And find me a mount," added Grant. "My own's up there by Jameson's and I don't dare go after it."

"Of course — you're such a stickler for regulations," said Gunnison dryly.

The troopers formed quietly in a hollow beyond the far bank of the stream. Grant, mounted on a spare horse, nodded to the guide. "Stay by me and don't ask questions. All I want is to sight Sugar Loaf Mountain, this side of General Arnold's quarters. Understand?"

The trooper nodded. Grant raised his arm, dropped it, and the column moved silently off, keeping a stretch of rising ground between it and the windows of the white house where Jameson and Tallmadge still talked.

The sun set and shadows fell deep over the hills. Grant rode on through the night, fretting at each halt that the strength of the horses demanded. If he succeeded, if by a sudden swift dash he was able to seize Arnold's person what would the next step be? He would somehow have to hold him until the arrival of the Commander, who by then would presumably have had Jameson's letter. If he failed — That didn't bear thinking about.

During a halt late the following afternoon, Gunnison drew Grant aside. "Sure you don't want to tell me anything more?"

"No. The less you know, the safer you are if things go wrong for me. But here's what you're to do when we sight the Robinson house above Sugar Loaf. Have your men mark where the guards are and be ready to disarm them. The guards won't be suspecting anything. Then — "

"Guards?" exclaimed Gunnison. "There are only a dozen men, and just a few of them on duty at one time."

"Then we'll bring our troop right to the door. I'll go in alone and you surround the house. If I come out with Arnold, have your troopers seize him. If he comes out alone — " he paused, "if he comes out alone, use your own judgment."

"Hold him and wait for further orders from you?"

Grant shook his head. "If he's alone, I won't be around to give any. I hope you'll arrest him. That's all I can tell you. Damn it, haven't those horses rested enough? Come on, mount up." And on they rode through the night.

It was well past dawn when the high peak of Sugar Loaf rose over the trees that choked the wild, tumbled valleys, a lowering overcast morning. "There she is," observed the sergeant who had acted as Grant's guide.

"Know just where the house is?" Grant asked.

"Ought to. Been here often enough."

"Then take your bearings. I want to come in from the shore side, and I don't want our troop to be seen until we're right there. Do you know a way?"

"Cart path they use for bringing in firewood from the hills," answered the sergeant. "Kind of curves in past the sheds and around to the kitchen door."

Sugar Loaf towered at the left as they rode on through the trees. Then the trees stopped and Grant saw a squarish house with a long, low ell jutting from the northern end. Smoke rose from two chimneys, eddied sluggishly and rolled away west toward a break in the Hudson cliffs where a gentler slope, scarred by a path, led to the river. Grant held up his arm, glanced at Gunnison who began cautiously shifting his troopers preparatory to surrounding the house.

Grant dismounted, drew a loaded pistol from his holster, took a deep breath and strode toward the low veranda. On all sides he could hear a muted thud and jingle as Gunnison's men deployed. By the corner of the house, Grant stopped. A horse was tethered to a post by the far end of the ell and even at that distance he could make out a big white "2" on the blue saddle cloth. Jameson's courier to Arnold had arrived!

There were no guards in sight. As Grant sprang onto the veranda, the front door opened and a fine-looking man in artillery blue and red stepped out. Grant's heart gave a great leap. Alexander Hamilton! If Hamilton were here, then the Commander must be nearby.

Grant called, "Colonel Hamilton!"

Hamilton smiled. "Oh, you must be Ledyard. Got anything for me from Tallmadge?"

Grant spoke quickly. "The Commander, Colonel. Where is he? It's urgent."

"He's inspecting some of the river forts with General Knox."

"The Commander had no courier en route from Colonel Jameson?"

"Jameson? No. We left Hartford much earlier than we expected, coming by the Northern route."

Grant felt a sudden hollowness. Jameson's courier had taken the southern road, and thus missed meeting Washington. Grant pointed to the horse with the 2nd Dragoon saddle cloth. "Whose is that?"

"That? Oh, that's another Jameson courier, I suppose. Came in not long ago with a letter for General Arnold."

"Did you see the general read the letter? What did he do?" Grant's voice was husky with growing shock.

Hamilton laughed. "What is this? Are you cross examining the general? Why, he didn't do much of anything, Ledyard. Read it, stuffed it in his pocket. Then he went upstairs, to speak to Mrs. Arnold, I guess. When he came down he told me that he was called across to West Point and that he'd see the Commander on his return." He smiled again. "Any more questions?"

"Sorry, Colonel. I should have said this concerns Culper."

Hamilton looked astonished. "Yes, you should have said so, I think. The general went down that path there. His barge's at a private landing by the cliffs. You might catch him if you hurry. I'd — Hi! Wait a minute."

Grant had already jumped from the porch. Forgetting Hamilton, forgetting Gunnison and his troopers, he set off down the twisting path at a full gallop. Then a rickety landing swayed before him. Immediately in front of him, the river was empty. Fifty yards away to the left, a dozen oars winked, dipped, winked as they drove a heavy barge downstream with the strong current towards Teller's point where His Majesty's sloop *Vulture* waited. The oars flickered on as Grant stared at the barge. A cloaked figure in the stern sheets turned, looking back at West Point, then at the Robinson house. Even at that distance, Grant recognized Arnold. With a sudden desperate gesture, Grant raised his pistol and fired. The ball hissed away over the water, splashed harmlessly a few yards short of the barge. In the stern a hand lifted in a gesture that might have been contemptuous derision. The oars pulled on and the barge grew smaller and smaller as it shot away to the shelter of the *Vulture*.

Grant wearily set his horse back up the steep path. When he reached the house, Hamilton was still leaning against one of the thin, square supports of the veranda. "Catch him?" called Hamilton.

"No," said Grant flatly.

"You saw the barge and General Arnold?"

"I saw the barge. It wasn't heading for West Point. It was pointed downstream and going fast."

Hamilton's head jerked back. "Downstream? By God, he might

run into a British patrol boat. Are you sure General Arnold was in it?"

Grant looked up. "General Arnold. Or Gustavus. Or Mr. Moore. It doesn't matter now."

Hamilton came down from the veranda with one long, slow stride and caught Grant's bridle. "Do you know what you're saying?"

"Yes. Arnold was warned by that letter which just came. We tried to stop it, Tallmadge and I. Another letter was on the way to the Commander, by Jameson's courier. If Washington had received it, he might have been able to catch Arnold before he escaped."

"What's all this? I've had no word from Tallmadge and I know the Commander hasn't."

"It all happened too fast. They caught John Anderson yesterday. He had treasonable papers. They're on their way to the Commander, too."

Hamilton's face was a mask. "John Anderson!"

"Anderson is Major John André. Now Gustavus has escaped." Weariness and bitter disappointment and a paralyzing apprehension for the future numbed Grant's brain and tongue. He saw incredulity creeping over Hamilton's face. He went on harshly, "No mistake. You see, I saw André when I went to Oyster Bay. I saw him as Anderson yesterday. There's no guessing."

Hamilton muttered to himself. "Arnold — Gustavus." Then he spoke more briskly. "We'll have to plan at once what to do. You stay right here until the Commander comes. I'll send a galloper after him."

"No," said Grant thickly. "Until Jameson's other courier arrives, I can't tell the Commander any more than I've told you. I want to get back to Tallmadge at once."

"Why Tallmadge?" asked Hamilton in surprise.

"Got to talk to him. Got to do something. Arnold's heading for the *Vulture*. He'll go to New York. We've got to find some way of warning Culper."

Hamilton said quickly, "Of course. Culper and those who work with him. Something's got to be done. But I'm sure Arnold never knew about Culper."

"We can't take a chance," said Grant with a shudder, remembering the letter that he had started to write to Arnold at Redding Ridge. "With your leave, Colonel, I'll start for Northcastle. My troops can follow at leisure."

Hamilton looked at the troopers who were beginning to appear around the corners of the house. "You certainly brought a big enough escort with you."

"Hoped I'd need them. Planned to arrest Arnold."

"Arrest Arnold? Whose orders, for God's sake?"

"My own. Tallmadge wanted to, but Jameson threatened *him* with arrest."

"So you were going to — Well, I'll be damned. Really, you'd better stay and talk to the Commander. He'll have questions, and — "

A trooper rode around the north side of the house and slipped from a stumbling horse. He shouted at Grant's men, "Where's the Commander? God damn, I covered about four states looking for him and Colonel Jameson'll give me hell."

Grant pointed to the newcomer. "The second courier from Jameson, Colonel. He's bringing the papers found on Anderson and the same letter that Arnold got. The Commander doesn't need me now. Good-by." Looping his reins over his arm he trudged wearily toward the rear of the house calling, "Gunnison. Give me your freshest horse. Bring your men back to Northcastle any way you like. I'm pushing on ahead."

All through the long, lonely ride back to North Salem, Grant's mind was dull with a sense of failure. For a whole day and a part of the next he could think only of Arnold in New York; Arnold closeted with Clinton and pouring out secret details of the Continental Army, its leaders and the men who filled its ranks. And did the traitor know about Culper and those who worked with him?

At the North Salem camp he found Tallmadge standing in the noon sun outside a little clapboard house, flicking at late wild-flowers with a small crop. He dropped the crop as Grant rode up. "What happened?" asked Tallmadge quickly.

"Got away," said Grant tersely.

"So I'd heard from the Commander's last courier. I'd hoped — "

"Did he tell you I'd been at the Robinson House?"

"No."

"Then how did you know it?" asked Grant.

Tallmadge smiled grimly. "I've seen enough of you to know what you would do. I guessed while we were talking with Jameson. That's why I stopped arguing." His face was set. "The letter from Jameson warned him, of course."

"Just that. Damnation, what a man! Hamilton told me he didn't turn a hair. Walked calmly off, leaving his wife and family in our hands. I got to the wharf not long after he'd pushed off. I was fool enough to try a long pistol shot at him. Missed, of course. How about his wife? Really, she amounts to a hostage. How much of the story do you know, anyway? I haven't heard any more."

"Well, as far as Mrs. Arnold is concerned the Commander will never harm her. You know that. So does Arnold. She'll probably be sent on to join him." His mouth tightened. "As for him — as soon as he got to the *Vulture* he had *his own* bargemen seized as British prisoners of war. Got five pounds a head for them."

"It's enough to sicken a polecat," said Grant. "But go on — what about André?"

"Well, he's told us the whole story. He was landed on the west bank of the Hudson by that damned *Vulture* that's been hanging down the river. He met Arnold the night of the twenty-first just outside our lines and the two went over everything, perfecting the plans for the betrayal. Arnold gave André those papers we found on him. But this meeting took too long. The *Vulture* was fired on

175

by one of our shore batteries and dropped downstream. The boatmen refused to row André to it. So Arnold persuaded André to
get into civilian clothes, cross to the east bank and make for the
British outposts. He sent a man named Smith with him. But
Smith got scared and left André at what he thought was a safe spot
outside our lines, in the Neutral Zone. Then, as it seemed, all the
major had to do was to keep walking until he met a British patrol
or outpost. Instead, by the worst possible luck for him, those prowl-
ing militiamen nobbled him up and you know the rest of the story."

"Damned if I do," said Grant. "Why didn't André take cover
when he saw the militiamen?"

"Why? Because one of them had on an old Hessian coat. You
remember it. André thought they were Tories and naturally ran
to them. Then it was all over, of course."

"Just the same," Grant went on, "There are more puzzles about
this, particularly in the early stages. Why did Arnold send that
broadcast letter about passing André — you know what I mean. I
got one. So did Sheldon and Jameson."

"Because, those letters were written a long time ago and were
delayed in transmission. At that time Arnold knew André was
coming, but he didn't know how. Hence he notified all possible
posts to be sure that André would be brought to him at once. Why
he wrote James and not John Anderson, I don't know — slip of
the pen? A possible way out for himself if things went wrong? I
don't pretend to be able to fathom Arnold's mind. All we know is
that it did happen, and it failed."

"What are we doing — the army, I mean?"

"The whole force is mustering around Tappan on the west bank,
ready to move up to the Point. But I think there'll be no attack by
the British. Clinton will know that we're warned. What a damnable business. And poor André is here with us. I've been seeing a
lot of him. He's all you said, and more. At first I thought he was
just facile, superficial. But there's a lot more to him. He's got courage, a sort of gay, calm courage and he's clean all the way

through. I'd give a lot, Grant, for a tithe of that courage."

"Has he admitted his identity?"

"Oh, yes. He's written the most straightforward, frank letter to the Commander. I tell you the Commander'll be damn well touched by it. Of course, he claims that he's a prisoner of war, that he came into our lines at the invitation of one of our officers."

Grant frowned. "I wish he hadn't taken that line. After all, he came, knowingly, at the invitation of a man whom he knew was going to betray us."

"What else can he say? He hopes, I think, that there'll be a legal point about invitation."

"It just won't hold, Major," said Grant. "He — why, he's in exactly the same position I'd have been in if things had gone badly for me at Oyster Bay. Within the enemy lines and out of uniform. There's only one answer."

Tallmadge looked sharply at Grant. "No doubt. But if you're called to testify before a military court, will you press for the extreme penalty?"

"No!" said Grant without hesitation.

"Of course not. You know him. Neither would I. By the way, Grant, he's been given quarters in that brick-ended house on the corner. I think it'd please him if you paid him a call. He's talked a lot about you. Come along. I'll pass you by the guard at the door."

When Grant entered the comfortable pine-paneled room, André was seated by the window, busily sketching one of his guards who sat astride a chair. At the sound of the opening door, André sprang to his feet. "Ledyard! This is kind of you, uncommon kind. Do sit down and have a glass of wine with me. Colonel Sheldon sent me some Madeira." He smiled at the posing guard. "That'll do for the moment, and thanks for your patience. Bring out a glass and that fresh bottle for Captain Ledyard. And by all means take a glass for yourself when you're off duty."

The trooper uncorked a bottle and poured wine for Grant and André. Grant raised his glass. "Your health, Major, and good fortune."

"And yours, Ledyard. Jove, it's damned odd to see you here, with our positions so reversed. Though we didn't nobble you at Oyster Bay. I swear I hadn't the slightest notion then that you weren't interested in hay. Nor had Simcoe. Aren't the Townsends delightful? And that little Polly Morgan."

"I thought them charming," answered Grant. He sipped his wine. "I hope everything's being done for you that can be done, Major."

"I'm under new obligations all the time," exclaimed André. "They even allow me to sketch." He caught up some sheets from the table. "Look at these. Do you think I've caught my guard's expression? His face is an interesting one. Very Yankee. Good solid bone structure under the skin and muscles, steady eyes, good chin."

Grant studied the sheets. With a few bold lines, André had sketched out the very essence of the man, keen, alert and with a suggestion of restrained cavalry swagger. "Excellent, Major. How the devil do you do it?"

"You really like it?" asked André eagerly. "I — I'd be most happy if you'd accept it as a memento of our meetings — official and otherwise." He took the sheet and wrote rapidly on it, handed it back to Grant.

Grant read: "From a soldier to a soldier, from a friend to a friend. To Captain Grant Ledyard, United States Dragoons from Major John André, A. G. to Sir Henry Clinton." He looked at André, deeply moved. "I'll value this, Major. Value it greatly and — "

André waved his thanks aside. "I'm so glad it pleases you. You know, I've thought a lot about you since I recognized you on the road the other day and realized what our earlier meeting really meant. I never could have done what you did at Oyster Bay. I should have been in a panic."

"I was," said Grant, "all the time. Even when enjoying your frothed chocolate."

André beamed. "It was good, wasn't it? I wanted to make some for Major Tallmadge but I couldn't find the ingredients. What a charming man he is. He's the sort of man you'd always be glad to have across a table or in a tight corner with you. But then, I've met so many agreeable people here in your army."

Grant was silent as he thought of Arnold. Comfortably housed in New York, while his pawn André was under heavy guard here in North Salem.

"Of course, I've got to be treated as a prisoner of war," said André earnestly. "I entered your lines in uniform. I shouldn't have let them persuade me to change to these clothes or carry those papers."

"But there's one thing that rather troubles me, Ledyard," André went on. "It's not that I question the justice of any board before which I appear. It's that its members, not being professional military men, may not be conversant with law and practice and custom. It could be important."

"Don't worry about that," said Grant. "The Commander's very well versed in such matters."

"But custom, tradition, European usage," muttered André.

"There again you're safe. You've the Marquis, von Steuben and Villefranche."

"Jove!" cried André. "Really, Ledyard, you cheer me immensely. I'm told that I'm to be transferred to headquarters at Tappan and that my friend Tallmadge will escort me with his dragoons. I do hope you'll ride with us. For one thing, I want to make a sketch of you and Tallmadge together to send to my family. They'd be so interested."

Grant rose hurriedly. "I — must be going now, but I'll try to look in on you again and — and — "

He got out of the room somehow and walked, unseeing, out into the sunshine that lit up the bright valley of the Titicus.

I X

The Desperate Gamble

In the second week of October, Grant jogged wearily into Fairfield after a perfunctory inspection of the posts to the east. For some days he had driven himself relentlessly, trying to erase from his mind the knowledge that John André had been hanged and of the part he himself had played in the events that led up to the tragedy. Militarily, there had been no other possible outcome. Yet Grant could not forget the boyish major and the hours they had spent together on Long Island and in Westchester.

His horse shied on the narrow road and he looked up irritably. Then he saw that a chaise was blocking his way, a chaise that he knew. He cantered up beside it and touched his helmet. From under the raised hood of the vehicle, Laurel looked up at him. She smiled, then a mask settled over her face. Grant said quickly, "I just wanted to be sure that you don't believe I was responsible for the Hilton affair."

Her eyes dropped. "I don't know what to think. Mr. Hilton was so sure."

"That's no evidence. You took his own hurried impression against my word of honor."

Laurel set her chin. "Your word of honor would be enough, as a person. But in your profession, you may not be free to speak the truth." She paused, then went on in a low tone. "If only you weren't part of all this. You don't belong in this cruel life. Then there's another thing. I've heard that you were responsible for the hanging of an innocent man, Major André."

Grant winced. "He was not innocent. He would have ruled against me under the same conditions."

"But those conditions!" she cried vehemently. "They have nothing to do with your real self. They're barbaric. Yet you live under them. The man you hanged — "

Grant turned his head. "I'd rather not talk about that," he said shortly.

"All right, Grant. But I do want to talk to you about all these people who have suffered so much. Could you spare the time to come up the Aspetuck? Four new families have refugeed from Westchester and we've got to look after them."

"You're sure you want *me* to help with them?" Grant said acidly. "A man whom you probably still think burned out the Hiltons, whom you charge with having a hand in the hanging of a so-called innocent man? Better ask one of your less warlike neighbors up the valley."

Laurel flushed and bit her lip. "I'm only thinking of those people, Grant. Helping them might make you forget the other things that you've done or might have done. This is one ground on which we can meet, you and I. You want nothing from these people and neither do I. It's common humanity. I — I didn't think I'd have to plead with you on that score."

Her voice died away and Grant thought he saw her chin quiver. He bent from the saddle. "I'll come, Laurel. You're right. That's our meeting-ground, as you said."

Laurel bowed her head, then looked up at him with a gentle smile. "I didn't mean to remind you about Major André. Please forgive me. But when Mr. Boyce — "

Grant started. "Boyce? What about Boyce?"

"The Boyces? I thought you knew them. The Isaiah Boyce family, just down the river from us. I'll ask Mrs. Boyce to come up when you're with us next time. I think she'll help us. Now good-by, Grant. I'll expect you."

The chaise turned onto a side road and Grant kept on into Fairfield. "Damn, but that gave me a start. Boyce! Of course, there are Boyces in every state. Couldn't be Dan Boyce. I can't be looking for spies under every bush and besides — Hold on! How the devil did Laurel know I had anything to do with André — or even who André was?" He wondered what Laurel really wanted. Were these destitute families merely an excuse? No matter. Her invitation promised a pleasant interlude for him.

Grant's feeling of depression returned. What move would the British make now, with Arnold whispering at the elbows of Sir Henry and his staff? What had happened to Culper? If Arnold had had the least hint of the doings of the merchant Robert Townsend in the city, of his family at Oyster Bay or of Abraham Woodhull at Setauket, those people would be quickly snapped up.

When he reached his room at the Oxbow, Caleb Brewster was waiting for him. There was a large wooden box on the table. "Spanish wine," Caleb announced. "From Setauket."

"No!" cried Grant. He ran eager hands over the box, noting that the boards were loose and that the nailheads showed the lid had been lifted. "I'm afraid this can't tell us anything, Caleb. Wine's no stuff to send letters in."

Brewster drew a heavy-bladed knife, slipped it under the boards and pried them up. Six squat bottles lay in a bed of straw, light glinting on their long, wax-covered corks. He carefully counted from a mark on the inside of the box, drew out the fourth bottle. With his knife he tapped the wax that sheathed the cork until it fell to the table, bit by bit. "Austin explained this to me on the beach," he said. "Hope I'm doing it right." The upper shaft of the cork showed clear of wax and Brewster neatly split it.

Grant snatched up the wad of thin paper that dropped to the table, "Hell and pitch!" cried Brewster. "It's blank. And we haven't got the stuff to bring out the writing."

Grant drew two small vials from inside his jacket. "Tallmadge gave me this and the code before I left North Salem. Caleb, be sure the door's locked."

Brewster turned the key in the door. "About time someone besides Tallmadge and Hamilton had those vials."

Grant's hand shook as he brushed liquid over the paper, then slanted it toward the light.

"Steady. We'll see the writing in a minute. There it comes," cried Grant. "It's from Culper."

The lines stood in bold relief. "The troops in their camps are being dispersed. No longer remaining under arms. North river flotilla likewise dispersed."

Grant looked up at Brewster. "There's one worry gone. They're not going to move against West Point."

"Seems so. For the moment, anyway. Hey! You're missing something here." He caught up the brush and flicked it over the paper below the last line. More words appeared. The sentences seemed to have been added as an afterthought, but they were unequivocal. "I am happy to say that I have been assured on most reliable grounds that Arnold does not know my name. Moreover, to my certain knowledge, no person has been taken up upon his information."

Grant lit a candle and carefully burned the letter. "The secret road stays open. Arnold knew nothing about Culper."

Brewster dropped into a chair. "That's one big relief, Grant. Just the same," he went on, frowning, "there's a lot of odd things going on right here."

"You mean that leak through Fairfield and Westchester?"

"Yes. A few nights ago I sent four whaleboats across to Mount Misery Point, just east of Setauket. I'd had word that there were royal stores that might be worth destroying." His voice grew harder. "No stores. When the landing party came back to the boats, they found the boat guards scuppered and musket fire coming from the high ground beyond the beach. Not many of the boys got back. That very night people from across the Sound landed east of the Housatonic. A little later, more landed beyond the Saugatuck. The point is those landings happened at the *one* time both those stretches of coast were clear. Grant, they knew something, knew it right down to the very day, hour, minute and second."

Grant sighed. "Nothing to do except keep watching. Be sure your men report every damn thing they see that might be suspicious."

Brewster grunted. "They tell me about every clam that squirts along the flats, especially now since they've heard about Arnold." He lowered his voice. "I tell you, the worst part of the whole thing is it's got all of us looking over our shoulders. I sent one of your gallopers on to Alex Hamilton with some news a day or so after I'd heard. I tell you, it made me sweat. Oh, yes, you're thinking that Alex is all right. Of course he is. But a month ago wouldn't you have said the same thing about Arnold? Suppose I get orders to move out of here, in person, from General Knox. God damn it, I'll obey — but I'll be wondering and so will my men."

"I know, I'm still skeptical about Jameson insisting on sending that letter along to Arnold," Grant said as he carefully stowed away his vials. "There's another thing, too. That time I was knocked out carrying the orders that were supposed to be captured, I heard a girl's voice. I'm sure I did."

"I remember your speaking about it once. Maybe you did hear a girl. Any idea who it could have been? You know most of the people around here now."

Grant shook his head. "Don't think I haven't wondered. There is one girl who's always riding about the country. She's asked me more questions about military things and people than a girl normally would."

"Questions?" Brewster sat up quickly. "By God, that may be the one. Why haven't you spoken of her? She may be part of the leak."

"Calm down, Caleb. This particular one couldn't be."

Brewster eyed him suspiciously. "Someone you're interested in?"

"Lord, no. I don't like her. But it's that flibbertigibbet, Rosa, Jethro Hollis's daughter."

"Oh, forget it," said Brewster with a gesture of disgust. "Say the man in the moon's doing it and I'll listen, but none of old Hollis's brood. Well, I'm off for Black Rock."

The fare at the Oxbow was meager that night and Grant did not stay long at the crowded table. Picking up a candle, he mounted to his room, his mind returning again to Laurel, her mention of the name Boyce and her knowledge of the André affair. He closed the door carefully and set the brass candlestick on the mantel. Then he started, staring at the folded letter propped on the white wood. He had locked his door when he left for supper. It had been still locked on his return, yet there was the letter.

It was addressed in an odd, slanting script to Major Benjamin Tallmadge, the Oxbow Inn, Fairfield in Connecticut. Below the address was written, *"For his eyes alone,"* the words heavily underscored. He had always disliked opening such letters, despite Tallmadge's insistence that he examine all communications. He broke the plain slab of sealing wax and sat down by the candle to read:

> As I know you to be a man of sense . . . you are by this time fully of the opinion . . . real interest and happiness of America lies in reunion with Great Britain . . . I have taken a commission in the British Army and invite you to join me with as many men . . . you shall have the same rank you now hold in the cavalry I am about to raise. I shall make use of no arguments to convince you . . . your own good sense will suggest everything I can say on the subject. I will only add that the English fleet has just arrived with a very large reinforcement. I am, Sir,
>
> Your Humble Servant,
>
> BENEDICT ARNOLD

Grant rose with a jerk, clapped on his helmet. He had to share his deep fury with someone, he had to thrust the mysterious sheet into another's hands, watch him read it and see an exploding anger that would match his own. Caleb Brewster was nearest.

He clattered down the hall. In the passage to his left a door squeaked gently and a bar of light fell full across his face. He heard a thick whisper. "See? I told you. Been here all along." The door closed as gently as it had opened.

Grant dropped his saber, worried out his double-barreled pistols and strode to the door, banging on it with a pistol butt. "Open up!" he shouted.

He thought he could hear a gentle rustling, a low hissing as though people moved cautiously in the room. He braced his shoulder against the panels, heaved as hard as he could. The wood gave a little, but the frame held firm. Measuring as well as he could in the darkness, he lowered the muzzle of his right pistol until it was opposite the lock, pulled one trigger, then the other.

The twin explosions seemed to shake the whole house, two blinding flashes blurred his vision as the door gave, swung inward. His remaining pistol raised, he kicked the door wide open, still blinking from the flashes. A voice bleated, "The candle! Knock over the candle!"

The window was wide-open. One man was through it, balancing on the sloping porch roof just outside. Another, short and squat, had one leg inside the room. He made a wild sweep at the candle and darkness swallowed up the room. Grant shouted, "Halt!" The candle on the floor gave a sudden flicker and Grant caught it up. The flame steadied, swelled, lit up the window and the face of the man who was backing out onto the roof. It was Dan Boyce.

For an instant Grant and Boyce froze, staring. Then Dan caught up a book from the window table and hurled it. It struck Grant on the arm and the candle flew across the room, its light guttering out for good. Grant sprang forward, caught the sill and tried to scramble through but his spurs tripped him. When he recovered his balance he saw Dan Boyce poised at the far edge of the roof. Boyce jumped, caught the elm branch that grew close and swung off into the night.

When Grant clambered out on the roof, he could just make out Boyce racing east across the Green, an awkward, long-legged man sprinting on ahead of him. Grant leveled his pistol, picked the nearer of the figures and fired, fired again. Boyce kept on running, but his lanky companion threw up his arms, spun about, took a few staggering steps and then pitched to the turf. Boyce ran on.

The smoking pistol still in his hand, Grant walked up the gentle slope of the roof and into the room. He saw Mr. Moobie gaping stupidly at him, a small lamp held high. Behind him Grant made out the frightened heads of a few maids. Mr. Moobie quavered, "Now Captain Ledyard! It's a nice, quiet house that I keep. I don't hold with shoutings and explosives."

Grant took the lamp from Mr. Moobie. "Send your people to bed," he snapped. "Come in and close the door!"

Without waiting for an order, the heads behind Mr. Moobie vanished and Grant heard their feet clattering on the stairs. Grant set the lamp beside the pistols. "This is old Mrs. Grannis's room. Who was in it?" he snapped.

Mr. Moobie twisted his hands. "Who else but her own flesh and blood cousins."

"Cousins? Where's Mrs. Grannis?"

"Occupying a spare room at the Keene's, ministering to the little ones, while their elders have gone to New London. Oh, dear me! This will mean a new lock and a new panel and Mrs. Grannis is so particular."

"Never mind that! How do you know they were her cousins?"

"Didn't they tell me so with their own voices? That they did!"

Grant snorted in exasperation. "So they told you. What else did they say?"

"I don't rightly know, Captain. They seemed such good-willed men. And so concerned with you. They — "

"With me? What did you tell them?"

"Oh, the talk was among themselves in the stable yard. The tall one says, 'It's Ledyard, and I'll prove it to you.' The short set one says, 'Can't be. He's with our party.' And then the tall one, he says, 'I'll show you. Let's wait and you can see for yourself. Of course, it's a risk. Now that you've left that letter, I'd kind of like to stir away from here. But if you're set to lay eyes on him, I'll show him to you. We'll wait in our room. When he comes home, he'll be bound to start out again, along of that letter and I'll throw light on him as he goes down the stairs.' Then they go into the house together and that's the last I see of them."

"Have your stable boy bring my horse around at once, saddled and bridled." Grant turned on his heel, and strode into his own room. So Boyce had left the letter from Arnold. Then, reasoned Grant, he had been ready to return to Long Island. But his companion, probably a local Tory, had said in effect, "Don't worry about the letter. Captain Ledyard will send it on to the major." Some such remark must have led to the conversation reported by Moobie.

In his own room, Grant caught up a pen. On a half-sheet of paper he wrote carefully, consulting from time to time the seemingly innocent dictionary from the cupboard.

721
NWUV AQ 728 EV KPGI 723 CP HEPAIL JLQN 178
730

He folded the sheet, stuffed it in his pocket along with the Arnold letter and started down the stairs. Over on the Green, men with lanterns were bending over a body. Grant made out the figure of Ralph Nelson, one of the local committee stumping about on his peg-leg. Nelson looked up as Grant halted. "Bad business, Captain. Know anything about it?"

"Line of duty," said Grant. "Who is he?"

"Lige Haskins. Used to live here, but moved to Stratfield before the war. Lige was a good man."

"He may have been a good man, but he was good for the king, not us."

"Lige! By God, never," cried Nelson. "He and his whole tribe are stanch. I know 'em."

Grant knelt by the body which was beginning to show signs of stiffening. Heedless of Nelson's protests, Grant searched the pockets of the worn clothes but found nothing of importance. He rose, wiping his hands on his saddle cloth.

Nelson said angrily, "Seems to me you're taking God's whole earth into your hands, Captain. Here's a dead man we all know, a matter for civil authority and here you go rummaging about him."

Grant shook his head impatiently. "We'll settle that later. He was helping the Crown tonight. He was — " A sudden thought struck him. "Did this man have a boat?"

"Sure he had one, not that it'll help him much now."

"Where'd he berth it?" asked Grant.

"Haskins' cove, west bank of the Poquonock River."

"Could he cross the Sound in it?"

"It's a dory with the mast forward. Lige could make Block Island or Hellgate fair enough."

Grant started off toward Black Rock at a gallop. Brewster was his only chance, if Dan Boyce were making for the cove on the Poquonock. Grant was sure that Dan would attempt to return at once.

The long peninsula slept quietly beside the still waters of the narrow harbor. As Grant rode down its length he could hear the low, whining complaint as Caleb's whaleboats rocked gently at their moorings. No light showed and Grant feared Brewster might have slipped out to sea on some mysterious errand. Then a man materialized out of the night and caught his bridle. "This way, Captain. In this hut."

Brewster looked up in surprise as Grant entered. "Hi! What's doing?"

"Plenty! Who's your best navigator?"

Brewster tapped his own chest.

"Then give me a quick answer. Say a man reaches Haskins' cove on the Poquonock a half hour from now, sails out and heads across the Sound. What chance would you have of cutting him off?"

"H'm. If God opened the pearly gates and poured out all the good luck that's stored up there, I'd say a fair chance, depending on the kind of boat your man had and how good he could handle her."

"The boat's a kind of dory, with a mast forward. As to the man, he may be a wizard or he may be a chuff," said Grant. "Here's the story."

He sketched out his first meeting with Boyce, then the latter's unexpected appearance at the Oxbow, his recognition of Grant. "So I figure, Caleb, he'll get across the Sound as soon as he can. I figure too he's got a horse hidden somewhere close by. That's why I said half an hour. He ought to be able to make the cove in that time."

"H'm. Yes, just about. What's he been doing in Fairfield?"

Grant started. "By God, I'd forgotten." He pulled out Arnold's letter. "He left this for Tallmadge. Read it, but don't explode. We haven't got time."

Brewster took the letter calmly enough. Then he sprang to his feet with a bellow of anger, upsetting the keg on which he was perched. Grant caught him by the arm. "I said we haven't got time to explode. Here's what I want you to do. There's no one in Fairfield now, but in about half an hour Sergeant Graves and two troopers will come in from Green Farms. Send that letter over to them and tell them to take it to Tallmadge at once. He's at Northcastle again. Also, take this." He handed over the half-sheet of paper on which he'd written his coded letter.

Brewster, still red with suppressed fury, nodded. "I see. But why do you want *me* to do this?"

"Never mind, now. Next, you have a good deal of contraband in the upper sheds. I want you to find a civilian rig. Then I want you to have as many of your boats as you think necessary to clear for sea. Caleb, we've got to stop Dan Boyce before he reaches the other side."

190

Brewster got to his feet and, opening the door, roared an order. "We'll try it, Grant. But it's a mighty long chance."

"It's got to be taken. Then the civilian clothes."

Brewster stared at him. "What for?"

"For me."

"Why'd you need that stuff to chase Boyce?"

Grant answered, "We might have to go ashore after him."

"Oh, by God, no! I agree I'd like to catch Boyce. But you — ashore in civils? Oh, hell's wrath, man. You, an officer in civilian clothes? With the British feeling as they must about what happened to André? No, Grant, for God's sake! We'll do our best to head him off, but that's all. If he lands, let him go back to New York and tell that limping bastard Arnold that he's delivered his letter."

"Can't do that, Caleb." He picked up the half-sheet of paper with the code message. "Tallmadge will approve of this. It reads: 'Must go to Long Island at once. Culper in danger from enemy.'"

"How does this affect Culper?" protested Caleb.

"Don't you see? Boyce saw me at Raynham Hall, fully accredited by Sir Henry. Now he has seen me in Fairfield as dragoon captain, he's heard about me. He'll go scudding back to New York. Can't you hear his questions at headquarters? Who gave this man his papers. That'll be easy enough to find out. Next — *why* was he given them and who suggested it? My God, it'll all lead to Culper, to Austin Roe, to Woodhull, to the other Townsends and their friends, not to mention the people whose names we *don't* know who work with Culper in New York. They'll hang higher than Haman, and a damn sight quicker."

Brewster paced about obstinately. "That's bad, of course. But how'll you stop it?"

"If we miss Boyce on the Sound, you'll land me. Have you heard from George Millis near the Nissequogue lately?"

"Got word last night."

"That's the spot, then. I figure Boyce will head for the Tory camp at Coram, and get transportation there. Likewise, he'll figure there's no hurry and he'll want to rest up a little. From Coram his route's pretty clear. Millis'll know who'll help us. It shouldn't be too hard to pick up Boyce's trail."

"H'm," said Brewster. "And when you catch up with Boyce?"

"I'll figure out something, then. Caleb — Boyce simply *cannot* reach New York. We can't let him."

Brewster got up and moved toward the door where he stood fumbling with the latch. When he spoke, his voice was oddly gentle. "Let's go find some clothes, Grant."

Two days later Grant was waiting impatiently in a shack near the shore. A gust of salt air swept in and Millis called, "You still in there?"

Grant gave a sigh of relief. "Right here, George, What news?"

Millis slammed the door behind him, lit a smoky lantern. "I've been moving. Brought you a fair parcel of tidings. First we found your man."

"Where?"

"To the big camp beyond Coram. He's still there. Seems he was wearied bad and he's laying over to rest."

Grant drummed impatiently on the table. "That's good to know. But the important thing isn't so much where *he* is as where what he knows is."

"He's sent no messages. No, Grant, I ain't guessing. You see, the man who's acting orderly to him's my cousin. Now for the rest. I've seen Woodhull at Setauket and no one's been plaguing him. Raynham Hall's quiet and the folks are too. Colonel Simcoe's not there but a few of the German boys are singing under Miss Sarah's window."

"We'll hear from Woodhull when Roe's expected?" asked Grant.

"If he's able. Likewise we'll hear when your Boyce slips his cable from Coram."

Grant picked up a rusty knife and began digging at the scarred edge of the table. "Do you have much trouble moving about?" asked Grant. "When I was here before you'd just been burned out and were hugging the beach pretty closely."

"Things is eased," answered Millis. "Folks forget quick. Another point that wouldn't hurt you to think about. The André business has set the British roaring. But — " he jabbed a scarred finger at Grant — "but what Arnold's done jarred a lot of home folks. I've passed the time with a few men lately, men who maybe wouldn't have minded taking a shot at me in a dark lane not so long ago. Now they're beginning to wonder. They're still king's men but they ain't so eager as they used to be. The Arnold trick don't taste good to 'em. Like my cousin to the camp near Coram, him that's valeting Boyce. In the past, we've shot at each other. Now we talk."

"Then you feel it's a little safer for unauthorized people to move about?"

Millis nodded in agreement. "A mite safer. Now we'll sup. I brought in some fresh bread and some tea and some prime lobster. Set the kettle on while I fix the lobsters. They're going to eat elegant."

Before dawn the next day, Millis started out and Grant was left alone in the shack. As the morning wore on, Grant walked up and down the beach, counting on Millis's assurance that it would be perfectly safe. He felt depressed and nervous. On his previous journey into Long Island, he had been buoyed up by exultation that cloaked everything he did with a sort of wild pleasure. Now the feeling was gone. His mission was essential. Failure would be only a little more horrible than success.

He had never known Dan Boyce well in college, but snatches of those days came into his mind. Dan singing "The Darby Ram" at the Blue Anchor while other students beat time with their mugs. Dan rushing past Grant in the Yard on a slushy, slippery morning and diving headfirst into the door of Harvard Hall while books and papers littered the melting snow. Dan and two brothers from Brookline Village rolling a heated cannon ball down the upper corridor of Massachusetts Hall. And now Dan was his enemy.

Toward noon, Grant made a big pot of tea and with its aid managed to swallow some salt beef and bread. Still sipping tea, he stood in the doorway looking out at the bright haze masking the Sound. Gulls marched in smug dignity along the sands in front of him, or swooping into the water, coasted with the tide.

Off to the right, two boys raced over the dunes, tossing a wooden ball back and forth as they ran. The more distant of the two seemed the stronger, for he kept throwing the ball over the head of the nearer boy, sending him scampering closer and closer to the shack. The ball lit a few feet from Grant and went skittering over the sand beyond him. The boy set off in mad pursuit, recovered the ball and threw it back to his companion, shouting louder than ever: "And Mr. Boyce is leaving Coram at daylight tomorrow. He's going by chaise. He'll be alone, he'll be alone." The shout became a sort of chant. "He's going by chaise at daybreak, by daybreak. Don't know which road—" The ball sailed to him, far over his head and he scampered off after it, still shouting.

The boys were gone and Grant stood staring at their footprints on the beach. Millis's precautions in getting the news to him seemed unnecessarily elaborate, but too much care was better than too little. He banked the fire, wrote, "The boys came by" on a slip of paper that he laid on Millis's blankets. Then he picked up an old horse collar whose stuffing was oozing through a rip on the inner side. The collar had been Millis's idea. Few people would think of challenging an obvious farmer lugging the collar to the nearest saddler.

Before shouldering the collar, Grant slipped off his coat and made sure that the two pistols were loaded, primed and secure in the leather harness below each arm next to his shirt. He put on his coat, hitched his right arm through the collar and left the hut.

The path was well marked over the dunes, rounding the salt marsh and ending at a shallow ford over the Nissequogue. In the farm yards that he passed, people barely glanced at him. One old man, coming out of an orchard with a sack of apples on his bent back, looked sourly at Grant's collar and snarled contemptuously. "Don't fix it. 'T ain't wuth it."

By mid-afternoon he reached Oyster Bay. The roof of Raynham Hall showed through the trees. He turned off down a side path that would bring him to the kitchen door. The servants were reliable and would be sure to remember him and bring him quietly to the master. The path was bordered by trees that were heavy with sickle pears, the branches bending so low that the ripening fruit bumped against Grant's head.

A gap in the wall on the right gave him a sudden glimpse into the stable yard. Men were dismounting. There was no mistaking Colonel Simcoe's ever-angry strong featured face, nor the Teutonic stolidity of the Hessian, Von Kittel, who seemed to be acting as his aide.

Simcoe was lashing about at nothing with a light switch. "Law be damned! This isn't Continental warfare. This is rebellion. For every hour they held André I'd hang a Yankee prisoner. For his death, I'd hang a score."

Grant waited, heart pounding, until Simcoe and the Hessian entered the house. Then he cautiously made his way out of the tree-edged path. Yes, the servants would remember Mr. Grant Ledyard. So would Colonel Simcoe and Lieutenant von Kittel. Raynham Hall was closed to Grant. As he walked blindly down a lane that branched from the side path, he caught the ripple of Sarah Townsend's laughter, the hearty voice of her father as they greeted the two officers. Grant's best move, he reasoned slowly would be to find a small boy willing to take a note to Mr. Townsend, asking him for a rendezvous outside the town.

The lane led through an endless series of orchards. To the left someone was singing under the trees. It was a song that André had sung one night in the garden of Raynham Hall. The song came nearer and the words rode to him on the notes:

If the heart of a man is depress'd with cares,
The mist is dispell'd when a woman appears...

Grant stepped to the wall. Among the rough boles a slim girl in a black dress figured with crimson was moving, reaching up every now and then for an apple which she dropped in the basket she carried. So far as he could make out she was alone in the orchard. Another step and Grant recognized Polly Morgan. He called in a low, carrying voice, "Excuse me, miss. Is there a saddler in this town?"

For an instant she stood staring. Then she came toward the wall. "A saddler? Oh, of course, that collar! Let me think. Oh, I know. Our freedman! He's really very clever. Climb over the wall and follow that little path. It'll lead you to the back of the house. Zeke's his name. Just tell him I sent you." She smiled graciously and drifted off through the trees.

Grant vaulted the stone wall, found the path and kept on eagerly, his step light and assured for the first time since he had left Millis's shack on the beach. The path turned from the orchard, burrowed through an arching tunnel of lilac bushes, wound around a rustic tool shed. Polly Morgan stood in front of it. She had evidently been running to cut him off for her breath came quickly. "Grant!" she gasped. "Why are you here? Why, *why* did you have to come again? I tell you, there's not the least chance of mercy if you slip. I've heard Colonel Simcoe and his officers talking."

"It's no worse than the other time, Polly."

"Oh, Grant, people are so much more alert now. And vengeful. Where are you going — or would you rather not tell?"

"First, I want word sent to Mr. Townsend. Can you manage that?"

Polly looked thoughtfully at him. "Mr. Townsend? Ye–es. But is it wise? I'm afraid people are beginning to wonder about him."

"Can't have that," said Grant. "But on the other hand, we may have to call on him. Polly, I'd better tell you why I'm here. Then we can reason things out."

She answered simply. "Grant, I'll do whatever I possibly can to help. Why don't we go into the house — I think it would be perfectly safe."

The little back parlor was cool and fresh with gleaming white paint on the woodwork and flowered curtains by its two windows. Polly settled herself on a mahogany sofa while Grant stood the horse collar against the wall and pulled a chair near Polly. As he told his story, Polly's face grew grave, but she sat motionless. "So you see," Grant concluded, "Boyce mustn't get to Sir Henry."

"Do you want to take him prisoner? How can you get him from the heart of Long Island to our lines?" Polly asked. Grant said nothing. She looked at him in deep bewilderment. Then all color left her face, and she seemed to withdraw into herself.

"You see," said Grant in a low voice, "I can't allow him to send a good dozen of our people to the gallows. If their work ends, the Commander will be blinded. We've got to keep the secret road open from New York to Setauket and Oyster Bay."

Polly's eyes met his squarely. "How can I help?"

"I think the best thing would be for you to see Mr. Townsend, risk or no risk. I need a few reliable men. Two roads have got to be watched. That's all."

"I wish we didn't have to bring Mr. Townsend into this," Polly's voice was a whisper.

"After all, this involves Mr. Townsend's son," Grant reminded her.

"Very well," said Polly. "I'll see him."

"You'd better tell him, too, that we've men watching the camp where Boyce will start from," Grant added. "The man who sheltered me along the coast has seen to that."

"I'll go now and — " the hoarse blast of a horn sounded in the narrow road outside the house, followed by the grind of wheels and the clop of hoofs. "Oh, dear," said Polly. "Another fish peddler. Excuse me while I tell him we don't need anything."

She slipped out of the room. Grant sat back in his chair, his mind working. Which road would Boyce take — the one through Flushing, or the lower one through Jamaica? Dimly he heard Polly's returning footsteps. But she was not alone. Heavy steps were following her. Grant got up quickly, one hand on a pistol butt. Polly stood in the doorway. "He — he said it was all right, Grant," she began.

"Couldn't be righter," said George Millis, as he followed her into the room.

"George!" cried Grant. "How did you know?"

Polly sank onto the sofa again with a sigh of relief as Millis set his heavy fish basket by Grant's horse collar. "Hated to startle the young lady," said Millis. "You see, Grant I knew you'd hit for Townsend so I went there. The stable boy saw and recognized you. I figured you'd come here."

"Good," said Grant. "What's your news?"

"First, Boyce has got to take the Flushing road. Seems the Jamaica road needs repairs bad. Some of the boys are tearing up a stretch. Boyce wouldn't dare take a chaise over it."

Grant glanced at Polly, who still sat primly on the sofa, listening intently. "Now another thing," Millis went on. "We've arranged for Boyce to travel with some of our people until he meets up with you."

"What then?"

George scratched his chin. "Seems like that's up to you, Grant. You're at the tiller, and it ain't for us to set a course. The boys'll do like you say. Any word you want sent 'em?"

Grant shook his head. "I'll have to improvise and they've got to be ready to act quick."

"You figured yet on how you're going to cross Boyce's course?"

"Not yet. I've got to — "

Polly spoke unexpectedly. She looked directly at Grant. "I know how. You could be my coachman."

Grant started. "I don't see how that would help."

George Millis raised a warning hand. "Steady, Grant. Let's listen to the young lady."

Polly spoke slowly, earnestly. "We have a coach and pair. People are accustomed to seeing me go about in it, and sometimes I've had to hire a driver for a day. A strange face on the box won't surprise them."

George gave a grunt of satisfaction. "Sounds all right to me, Grant."

Grant looked dubious. "Perhaps. But remember there are a few people around here to whom I wouldn't be a stranger."

"Like Colonel Simcoe?" asked Polly directly.

"Yes."

"I think we can take care of that. I doubt that he'd recognize you on the box — and anyhow if he leaves Raynham Hall, he'll probably take the Hempstead road. That's where the big camps are."

"I hope you are right," said Grant. He made a quick gesture as though brushing away a thought. "It's a gamble we've got to take."

"When do you want to start? Zeke will harness up, and I'll pack a basket as though I were taking things to friends in Flushing."

"No!" exclaimed Grant. "You're not coming. I'll take the coach and hit for the Flushing road."

Polly faced him, her chin determined. "Grant, that just won't do. I've got to be there to answer questions if you're stopped."

"Now if I was you," put in George, "I'd listen to the young lady."

"But if anything went wrong — " began Grant heatedly.

"Don't you see, Grant," cried Polly. "They're less apt to go wrong if I'm there. I know all the side roads, I know all the people."

"It's out of the question," said Grant. "I'll find some other way."

"Like what, if I ain't prying?" said George.

"Like anything but this. It's going to be a damned unpleasant business and Polly *can't* be involved."

Polly laid her hand on Grant's sleeve. "Will you stop being so gallant? We none of us count in this except for what we do. It's far too important. You said yourself that nothing else matters. Have you changed your mind? Just stop and think what all this means."

"No!" cried Grant. "I haven't changed my mind. But — oh blast it! You're right. It'll be better if you are with me."

"Now that's right close to being sensible," said George Millis, picking up his fish basket. "I'll sleep a mite easier tonight, and maybe I'll think up a prayer or two to say. You'll have news from me if there be any. Good-by, you two."

When George Millis and his fish were gone, Polly turned to Grant. "How'll we know what time to start?"

"George will send word. Don't worry about that."

"I'm not worrying about anything, Grant. You can spend the night in the coachhouse. There's a spare room next to Zeke's. Now I'll make you a sketch of the Flushing road and all the lines that lead into it."

Grant pulled up two chairs to the table while Polly got out papers, pens and ink. He watched as she became absorbed in her sketch, describing the lanes to him as if she were planning a pleasant drive through the country. "She can't realize what I must do," he thought. "Polly," he broke in gruffly, "do you realize what it means when I said Dan Boyce could not be allowed to reach New York?"

She looked soberly up at him. "Yes, Grant. I understand. Everything." Then she picked up her pen. "There's this path that leads to the southwest. It's just wide enough for the coach." Her voice went on, low and musical, and the two heads bent over the sketch.

Word from George Millis came at noon and Polly and Grant set off at once, with the basket of gifts for friends in Flushing placed conspicuously on the seat beside Polly. Now they waited impatiently in the little tree-choked lane that led into the Flushing road. That road was empty. There was no sign of Dan and his party. Grant stood at the junction, his eyes straining down the road as it twisted along the valley below. He glanced at the sun, already well down in the west. Something must have gone wrong. The sick hopelessness that had been mounting in him with the slow lapse of time deepened. Either Dan Boyce had managed somehow to pass on the Jamaica road, or perhaps he had started far earlier than Millis's message had said.

Grant walked down the lane to where the horses shifted uneasily. It was bad for them to stand hour after hour, bitted and bridled but Grant had not dared loosen so much as a buckle. Polly looked pale and drawn. Grant managed a reassuring smile. "Nothing in sight, yet Polly."

"Grant — what if we've missed him?"

"We've still plenty of time," he managed to say. "Why don't you open the hamper and pour yourself a glass of Madeira, Polly? You'll feel better then."

"Grant — if we've missed him — what happens?"

"But we haven't missed him, Polly. We must be patient a while longer. If he doesn't appear by sunset, you'll have to return to Oyster Bay and warn the Townsends. I'll push on to New York and find Culper, and —" He gave a sudden leap, caught up the reins and sprang onto the box. Far down the road he saw a light plume of dust and he could catch faintly the grind of light wheels over a pebbly surface. A horse appeared over a rise, then the hood of a chaise. Grant reached for the whip and shouted to Polly, "Hold on tight!" He swung the coach along the rutted lane, eased it skillfully out onto the road so that it was blocked. The chaise rolled on toward him, the driver waving his whip and shouting. Grant jumped down on the far side of the coach, tugged out both pistols. As he passed the window he called, "Keep down, Polly." Then he stepped clear of the rear of the coach, pistols raised, just as Dan Boyce, broad face ablaze with anger, jumped from the

chaise and ran toward him. "Damn your clumsiness! Clear the
road and let me pass!" Then he saw the pistols, and the red faded
from his face.

"Sorry, Dan," said Grant. "You're not going to New York."

Dan recovered himself quickly. "My God! It's Ledyard!" With
amazing agility he side-stepped, ducked, caught at Grant's right
hand. His fingers slipped off but the wrench was enough to twist
the pistol from Grant's grip. Boyce dove for it, but Grant shoul-
dered him away. He didn't dare fire for fear of hitting the coach.
With a swooping motion he retrieved the fallen weapon. "Better
come along with me, Dan," panted Grant.

"Damned if I will."

Grant had no idea where they came from, but all at once six
Hessians appeared, a sergeant in the lead. Boyce ran toward them
shouting, *"Hilfe! Hilfe!* Fire, for God's sake fire!"

Grant's pistols sagged to his sides and he stood gaping helplessly.
One Hessian pinned Boyce's arms and another bound him. "Hang
on to him," said the sergeant and clumped up to Grant. "He near
give us the slip, Cap. Good thing you blocked the road."

Grant gulped. "Who are you?"

"Friends of George Millis. We stuck close to this feller all day,
but he begun a slashing of his horse along the flats yonder." He
glanced at his companions who were testing the knots of Boyce's
ropes. "All right boys, strip. These duds ain't healthy no more."
He struggled out of his green jacket and tossed it into the bushes,
scaled his wide cocked hat after it. His men followed his example
and stood relaxed in ragged shirts and knitted sailor's caps.

"Where's George?" asked Grant.

"Watching the road back there a piece." He touched his cap as
Polly stepped from the coach. "My duty, miss. George spoke about
you. Now if I was you, I'd just set out for home again." He fished
a chunk of tobacco from his pocket, bit off a corner. "So
soon's you're out of the way, miss, we'll do what we come here
for."

Polly turned white under her bonnet. She laid a hand on Grant's arm. "There must be some other way." Grant looked down at her, at the desperate entreaty in her eyes. Then he looked at Dan standing quietly among his captors just out of earshot. He suddenly felt physically sick with the success of his mission. First André and now — in much rougher fashion — Dan Boyce. His voice was unsteady when he spoke. "Polly, you said when you started out that you knew what all this meant."

"I thought I did. But isn't there some other way? Why not hold him as a prisoner, turn him over to the Commander?"

Just then one of the men gave a shrill whistle, "Stand by, Bill. Something's coming."

All eyes looked to the west. Against the western glow a single pack horse appeared, another, a string of six pack horses, and bringing up the rear, a rider, a slight, spare man who rode with his head back as though whistling.

Grant cried, "Wait! That's Austin Roe!" He ran toward him, reaching out to catch the bridle, but before he could speak, Roe swung from the saddle. "My God, Grant, what the hell are you doing here?" he said hoarsely. "What's happening?"

"They've caught a man named Boyce. He's a spy for Clinton. He knows too much. If he ever gets to headquarters, he'll uncover our whole chain."

Roe said slowly, "That's bad. Well, I suppose there's only one thing to do." He glanced significantly at the armed men about Boyce.

"Damn it, Austin, I can't do it. What I want to do is get him across the Sound. Let the Commander decide. Besides, Boyce might give up some mighty valuable information."

Roe whistled. "That's a risk, a wicked risk, Grant. How do you figure on getting him to the other side?"

"Where are you going?"

"Setauket, of course."

"Meeting Brewster?" Grant asked.

"He'll be somewhere, I guess. But I've nothing for him. This is a bona fide shipment."

Grant smacked his hands against Roe's horse. "You guide us to Caleb and I'll guarantee to turn Boyce over to the Commander within thirty-six hours."

"H'm," said Roe dubiously. "We might bring it off, but — yes, you've got one point that's valid, so far as I can see." He remounted, whistled to his pack horses and started down the hill.

When Grant and Roe reached the bottom where the coach still blocked the road, the leader of Boyce's ragged guard came forward belligerently. "Get the young lady out of the way or we'll go ahead right in front of her," he said to Grant.

"There'll be no shooting. We want this man to talk — in the right place. We're going to take him to the Commander."

"Don't sound good to me," grumbled the guard.

Roe leaned from the saddle, arms crossed on the pommel. "He's worth more alive than dead, my friend."

The leader looked at Roe and nodded. "All right. If you say so, we'll leave him to you. Take him."

Grant walked on to where Boyce stood, bound, pale but somehow calm. "You'll come with us, Dan," said Grant. "There'll be no firing squad."

Boyce shivered violently and he closed his eyes for an instant. Then he looked squarely at Grant. "Thanks. Your doing?"

"Ours. You'll have to do just what we say. Will you give your word not to try to escape?"

"I can't do that, Grant. You wouldn't in my place," answered Boyce.

"No — but you'd have asked me, Dan. We'll have to take what steps we can to be sure of you." He nodded to the guards. "Just hold on a little longer."

When he reached the coach, Austin Roe had joined Polly, to whom he seemed no stranger. Polly said nothing, but her face was calm again, untroubled. "I've told Dan," said Grant. "Now,

Polly, if I turn the coach around so Austin can get by, can you drive home alone? I'm afraid it's the only way."

"No," said Austin. "I think our plan is better." He smiled at Polly. "We'll take Boyce in the coach with a couple of guards. He can't be so easily seen in it as in his open chaise. You drive the coach. I'll range along with my horses. Understand? If you are stopped, say you have a sick gentleman in the coach and you've joined up with me for mutual safety."

"And what about Polly?"

"She's going to drive Boyce's chaise until we meet Caleb. Don't worry. I'll find means along the road of getting word to her brother. Then, come morning, she'll drive to Oyster Bay along with some mighty safe people. She has thought it all out."

Grant began to expostulate, but Polly cut in firmly. "It's the only way, Grant."

"It's just not necessary for you — " Grant began. Then he turned quickly. "All right. When I've got the coach swung west, bring Boyce and his guard along. Arrange matters to suit yourself, Austin. You're in charge until we hail Brewster."

It was growing dark as the cavalcade topped the crest of the eastern hill. From the high box, Grant could just make out the bobbing top of the chaise and the pack horses that followed it. Austin Roe paced his single-mount close to Grant's nigh-horse. The wheels ground on, their sound mingling with the crunch of hoofs and the musical cling-clang of the bells on the pack horses. Then a man sprang from the bushes, gave a great leap and scrambled up on the box by Grant. It was George Millis. "Road's clear ahead," he said calmly.

"Don't do that again," said Grant irritably. "My God, I might have shot you, bouncing out like that."

From time to time the convoy halted under a night sky where thin clouds were slowly veiling the stars. In a shallow dip where the scent of salt marsh was strong on the steady breeze, Grant left George Millis in charge of the coach and ran ahead to the chaise.

Polly was sitting quietly, her chin cupped in her hand. She looked very tired. "Aren't we almost there?" she asked.

"Polly, I'm worried about your getting home."

"Mr. Roe's arranged for two of the guards to drive me. I'll be all right," she answered.

He passed his hand over his forehead. "We've been so lucky so far that I'm scared. We owe an awful lot to you, Polly. I'll see that the Commander knows."

"I? What have I done?"

"You've been a help from the very first. And you've been right, Polly. You've thought quicker and more clearly than any of the rest of us. Both George Millis and Austin were speaking of it at the last halt. You weren't thinking about yourself either." He took her hand, looked up at her profile vaguely outlined against the sky. "I often think of Oyster Bay. There were pleasant times. I try to think of just those parts. As for the rest — " he paused.

She turned her head toward him. "Yes, Grant."

A long, low call sounded from the column. He pushed himself away from the chaise. "Tell you later. That's Austin warning us to start." He pressed her hand again and ran back to the coach where George Millis made room for him on the box. "All quiet. George?" asked Grant.

"Quite. The feller inside's always calling for water. And he wanted me to be sure and tell you that he'd resigned his commission before he went over. That mean anything to you?"

"Plenty," said Grant. So Boyce had resigned before siding with the Crown. Then there could be no charge of desertion against him when he faced the Commander. That meant prison for Dan. Not a firing squad or the gallows.

It seemed to Grant that the road they were following curved rather deeply south, though it was hard to tell with no stars to guide him. Nonetheless, Setauket must be near. Austin rode his mount close by the front wheel. "Want to take a scout for me,

Grant? I'll ride by your horses and keep them moving, and on the road."

"Anything you say, Austin."

"Hop down. Can you make out that farm off to the right? There's a shed between us and the farm. A picket fence by the shed. There'll be milk pans airing there, slung on the pickets. Remember?"

"I'll be right back," answered Grant, running into the fields. On his first trip he had counted the number of bars down in a gate, the lights in a distant house. This time it was milk pans. Off by the farm a dog barked sharply, and was abruptly silenced. The fence. He worked slowly along it, hands feeling the tops of the pickets. Then metal rang under his fingers. He counted. One — two — three — four. That was all. He started to turn back, but his foot clanked against something in the grass. He reached down, felt the smooth inside of a pan. Four on the pickets, one on the ground. Austin had said nothing about the ground, but it was worth reporting.

He overtook the coach and made his report. Roe listened carefully. "H'm. That one on the grass — I'd forgotten. Was it close to the fence? Up-ended?"

"Both. Another thing, Austin. It couldn't have blown off. They're deep pans and they sat solid on the pickets."

"Four and one." Austin gave a satisfied nod. "I'm going up to the head of the column. I'll say good-by now. You'll turn where the chaise turns, down toward the beaches."

"Good-by?" echoed Grant. "You're not coming with us?"

"That fifth pan said no," answered Roe. "I'm to keep east. Don't worry about me."

"Where are we?"

"East of Setauket. Keep on and don't worry. You'll find Caleb's boats waiting. Tell him I'm faring on." He waved good-by.

Grant took the reins from George Millis. The latter looked at him in the dark. "Dropping the pilot? Must mean we're close to berthing," he observed. "Sure you know where you're pointing?"

Grant shook the reins and the horses broke into a weary trot. "Got a different pilot, that's all. All we have to do is stay close by the chaise and follow it." When its hood showed not far ahead through the darkness, he called, "Right behind you, Polly." She waved.

Grant saw the chaise make a sharp left turn and swung in behind it, keeping his span at a safe distance. They were on a sandy road that wound on down a long series of gentle terracelike slopes and the smell of the sea was stronger. A light breeze blew in from the north and set the stunted trees and low, wind-whipped bushes bobbing and nodding. There were fewer trees as the road led on, but the bushes seemed thicker and taller. Suddenly Millis braced his feet on the dash, snatched at the reins that Grant had already pulled taut. A few yards ahead the chaise had halted, and Grant just managed to swing his pair clear of it. Then he jumped to the ground. The two guards who had been keeping up with Polly ran back and took their posts by the coach. "Anything wrong, Polly?" cried Grant as he reached the chaise.

"No — it's only — see that single dead tree against the sky? And that white rock just by the side of the road? Mr. Roe said that's where we'd find — "

In the darkness to the right a pistol snicked and a muffled voice called, "Who's there?"

Grant sprang forward. "Caleb!" The bushes stirred and Caleb Brewster loomed huge in front of Grant and stood staring at him.

"Grant, by God! What's happened? Where's Austin?"

"He was with us, but he got a sign along the road and headed on east. Nothing for you in his convoy."

"So you got clear. God's fury, I never expected to see you again. Did you get any trace of him you were after?"

"We've got him, Caleb, in the coach."

Caleb's voice sank to a whisper. "In the coach! You — you *got* him?"

"Yes. Alive. Let's get aboard. How far from the beach are you?"

"No beach. A deep backwater behind these bushes. One whale-boat waiting, two more out in Conscience Bay."

"Far?"

"The backwater twists west to the Bay about a half mile. We'll start loading." He gave a low whistle and two men, muskets slanting over their shoulders, appeared beside him. Grant nodded and started for the chaise. George Millis materialized close to Grant. "We'll turn the coach, Grant, and I and the others will see the young lady gets to Oyster Bay."

"Fine, George. Now have the boys bring Boyce out of the coach. Caleb and some of his men are right over there. They'll take care of him." George slipped away toward the coach.

Grant called, "Polly!"

A voice at his elbow said, "Yes, Grant. I'm here."

"This part of your journey's over. I wish it weren't, Polly. I haven't had a chance to tell you half of what we owe you. If it hadn't been for you — "

"You'd have gotten along. But I'm glad if I helped a little."

"A little! Look, Polly, when I reach the other side, I'll get word to you through Caleb and Austin. I'll try to write at least some of what I haven't had a chance to say these last hours. You'll answer?"

"I'll try to — Oh!" she stepped back a pace.

Arms still bound, Dan Boyce was being led toward the bushes where Caleb and his men waited. As he passed, he said huskily, "I owe you this, Grant. They'd have shot me without winking."

"Good luck, Dan, and don't forget to tell the Commander about your resignation."

From somewhere off to the left, a high, furious voice called out, "Blast your thick skull, not yet!"

Grant reached for his pistols and swung about in the direction of the shout. There was a flash and the flat report of a musket. A bullet whined through the bushes. Then the same voice, "God stiffen you! You've spoiled it. At 'em, all hands!"

Grant caught Polly by the shoulders and swung her about. "Keep the horses between you and the flashes! Guards! Hurry that man along. Caleb! Get your men up here!" The bushes off to the right wavered and shook. He fired one pistol, heard a yelp of anguish, more thrashing. George Millis was shouting, "To port! There by the rocks!" and Grant heard him fire.

Caleb and a vague huddle of men dropped to their knees in the shelter of the coach and began firing off into the night. A flame spluttered some twenty yards ahead, flew high in air, dropped in a long, graceful arc, flared out into a bright yellow flame as the torch hit the ground. Grant darted past the chaise and collided with Polly. He put his arms around her, forcing her to the ground. "Lie flat. Back of the wheel, but keep clear of it. I'll stand by the horse so he won't bolt."

There were voices everywhere, some familiar, some strange. The whack-whack-whack of muskets sounded viciously. One of Boyce's guards was hit, and whirled about, clutching at his shoulder. Grant, the bridle in one hand, took a quick step toward Dan who, unguarded for the moment, gave a sudden wrench, and twisted free. Still bound, he ran clumsily toward the unseen attackers roaring, "For the Crown. On His Majesty's service! Help!"

Grant shouted, "Dan!" but the bound man plunged on, smashing into the bushes. Grant dropped the reins and ran on in pursuit. His foot caught a jagged root and he tripped, falling headlong. He yelled, "Caleb! Rush them! He's away — "

High and clear, off to the left, someone shouted hoarsely, "Out, cutlasses! This way!"

There was an answering cry. " 'Ware boarders! Coming over the side!" A confused scuffling broke out, rose, died away.

All at once there was a silence, a deep silence that was somehow accentuated by the dying flicker of the torch the riders had thrown. Caleb glided up beside Grant. "Gone, by God!"

In a dead voice, Grant answered, "So's Dan. We've failed."

"Can't be helped," snapped Brewster. "Just some damn gang of Tory prowlers who stumbled on us. What scared them off?"

"Someone yelling. Sounded as though he was leading a big board-ing party. Maybe more of your men. It doesn't matter. Dan's escaped. God damn it, Caleb. Let's round up all your men and start after them."

"No good. They've got the whole night to hide in." He caught up the torch. "Who's moaning there?" He moved off through the bushes, Grant following him. "It's worth the chance, Caleb," he urged. "They'll probably scatter and reform on the main road."

"And nip us like a pair of lobster claws. Where the hell are those groans coming from? Push those damn shrubs aside, Grant."

"It's still a chance. If we quit now, there's no chance."

"No chance any way. It's — Hell!" He stopped, held his torch higher. The light flared on a roughly dressed man who lay face down in a little clearing. Caleb knelt, turned the man over gently.

Then his breath went in sharply. "George! George Millis!" Grant knelt by Caleb, took the torch from him. "Look — it's only a scrape on the forehead, Caleb. Wipe the blood off. Splash your water bottle in his face."

Caleb rose slowly. "No, Grant. A bullet through his forehead and out the back of his head." His voice sank. "By God, Grant. *He* was that boarding party. He rushed their left all alone and they took a panic from it. He knew what he had to do and —" He bent, covered George Millis's face with the battered hat. "I'll send some of the boys after him. Can't leave him lying here."

Grant spoke unsteadily. "It's my fault. He was helping me. And I let Dan escape. Caleb, I shouldn't have come."

Caleb dropped a huge arm about Grant's shoulders. "You had to, Grant. It's bad, Boyce getting away, but we'll make out somehow, the whole lot of us." He waved the torch to keep it burning. "Come on. We've got to look farther. I heard groans. I —" He stopped suddenly, and knelt down by a thick clump of bayberry.

"It's Dan Boyce! And he's dead! Grant, you didn't fail."

The bullets, fired by the friends toward whom Dan Boyce had run, were less kindly than that which had snapped out George

Millis's life. "Hit twice," muttered Caleb while Grant stared down, sick and dizzy. "Twice. Not dead long. 'Twas his groans I heard, but the first shot must have stunned him."

"We — we'll take him along," said Grant.

"Not with George, we won't. The boys wouldn't understand it. Here he'll have to lie. Don't argue, Grant. I mind you knew him. He's at peace now as he never would have been alive, not if he'd reached a hundred. And what he knew is at peace with him. Clinton'll never learn it. There are people in New York and other spots that can sleep easier now. So can the Commander. Come along."

Grant paused, irresolute. Then he snatched Caleb's knife from its sheath and knelt by Dan's body. "At any rate, no one will find him this way." He slashed at the cords that bound Dan's arms, covered his face with his hat. For a moment he stood looking down at the body. Then he turned on his heel and ran back toward the chaise.

"Polly!" he called. "Polly!"

From the darkness her voice sounded, faint and shaken. "It's all been for nothing! Grant, what ever will we do? He's gone! Those people in New York! The Commander!" She moved toward him, her hands before her.

Grant caught them. "Steady, Polly. It's all over. His Tory friends shot him. Caleb found his body over there."

She gave a little gasp. "Dead? Oh, how terrible. Yet I suppose it's better this way. But, Grant, I'm glad neither you nor your men did it. Anyway, it's all over. Now you must get back across the Sound. Don't worry about me. George Millis and the others will see that I get home all right."

He shook his head. "Not George, Polly. He's the one who saved us all."

"Gone?" cried Polly. "George Millis? But he was the best of all. And two of our guards are dead, too!"

"I know. It's been a big price to pay, but the stakes were far bigger. Better get into the coach now. One of the other men will drive you — "

He whirled about. Far inland someone was shouting. A musket thudded with a bright flash. Caleb called through the darkness. "Come on, Grant, push off! Those damned Tories are coming back. Probably picked up some more friends. Hurry."

There was another flash and a dull report. The voices sounded nearer. Grant said thickly, "We can't send Polly back through all those people. We've only two guards left and they can't protect her. Polly, you've got to come with us, it's the only way. Quickly."

For an instant she was silent. Then she threw back her head. "Yes — you're right. I'll have to come with you, Grant."

"But your coach? The chaise?" cried Caleb. "They'll be recognized!"

A guard spoke nearby. "Don't fret about them, we'll head 'em inland, like we looted them. We may have to share them with them other fellers, but it can't be helped. They won't know which side we're on. Miss, I'll drop word to your brother when I sight Oyster Bay again." He scrambled onto the box and started the coach away from the water, another man driving the chaise. From the coach box, Grant caught a joyous bellow. "This way, fellers. Hey! Don't shoot. Got fifty pound worth of horse flesh and carts."

The musket shots and cries died away. Caleb exhaled noisily. "By God, he's drawn 'em off us for a while at least. Come on."

An hour later Caleb's whaleboat was in mid-Sound. In the stern sheets Grant sat contentedly. Polly, sound asleep, rested her head on his shoulder, the hood of her cloak pulled up to shield her face from the spray. Tiller under his arm, Caleb glanced across at Grant. "Getting lighter. We'll sight Fairfield by sunrise. Your little lady all right?"

Grant looked down at the white blur of Polly's face in the shadow of her hood. "All right? I've never seen her when she wasn't, Caleb."

Caleb Brewster nodded. "Don't guess you're ever apt to. Seems to me she's a pretty good soldier, Grant." He began to whistle under his breath as the sharp prow of the whaleboat drove on north toward the Fairfield beach.

X

The Midnight Visitor

Iᴛ was broad daylight when Grant and Polly walked past the charred houses of Fairfield, and up to the low porch of the Oxbow. At the wide door Grant stepped aside. "Here's Mrs. Moobie coming down the corridor. She'll look after you. When you're ready, she'll be glad to show you Major Tallmadge's room." With a smile Polly vanished in the wake of Mrs. Moobie, and Grant ran upstairs in search of the major. He was writing at the table by the window, but sprang to his feet at Grant's entrance. "I got your code message. In God's name what happened?"

As Grant threw off his tattered civilian clothes and put on his uniform again, he gave Tallmadge a quick account of Boyce and the capture on Long Island. When he had finished Tallmadge clapped his forehead. "Jove, but that was a close call. So Boyce is dead. Are you sure he talked to no one?"

"Pretty sure. George Millis's cousin was with him all the time at Coram. Some British officers tried to pump him, but he insisted that his news was too important to give to anyone but Clinton. I'd have done the same thing in his place."

"Seems safe enough," Tallmadge said. "Damn it, that was too bad about George Millis. We're going to miss him, I can tell you. Now in my report to the Commander, I'm stressing the fact that you went on this mission entirely on your own initiative, that you moved at once and without hesitation, that you took every conceivable step to insure its success. Whom else do you want mentioned?"

215

"Caleb, of course. And George Millis. Also the pseudo-Hessians. I have their names."

"That's all?"

"No. There's someone else, someone with the Moobies." Grant stepped to the door and called, "Mr. Moobie, is Miss Morgan ready to come upstairs?"

In a moment Polly appeared, smiled at Grant as he led her into the room where Tallmadge was still bent over the table. Grant announced, "Miss Morgan, may I present my superior officer, Major Tallmadge."

Tallmadge sprang to his feet. "Honored, Miss Morgan. May I offer this chair? I hope I can be of service to a friend of Captain Ledyard's." He seemed puzzled.

Polly seated herself, still smiling. "Thank you, Major Tallmadge. It is a pleasure to meet you. I've heard so much about you through my friends the Townsends."

"The Townsends!" echoed Tallmadge. "Then you — "

Grant broke in. "I went to her when I found that Simcoe was at Raynham Hall. She suggested the means of cutting across Dan's trail. She and George Millis worked out the way of getting him safely to the Sound after the capture. She was with us all the time, helping us. When the Tory raiders came back we couldn't leave her, so we brought her over with us."

Tallmadge gave Polly a long, steady look. Then he said, "With them all the time. I see." He rose and bowed to Polly. "My report to the Commander isn't complete after all. This part will be a pleasure to write, Miss Morgan."

"But I didn't do anything," protested Polly. "I was just with them."

Tallmadge smiled at her. "We'll let the Commander judge that. Now we've got to see about getting you home safely."

Polly looked small and demure in the big chair, her face serious in its frame of black hair. Grant said uneasily, "I suppose we'd better talk to Caleb about that. But she should have a few day's rest to recuperate."

Tallmadge rose and began to pace up and down. "Let me see if I have the matter clear in my mind. The men who attacked you near Conscience Bay will report that rebel partisans kidnapped Miss Morgan." He turned to Polly. "Where will people think that you were going?"

"Oh, that won't matter," said Polly eagerly. "We've never been questioned by the British, any of us. My story is that I was driving out of Flushing and was seized by rebel partisans."

"Do your people at Oyster Bay know that, so they can corroborate that you were in Flushing?" asked Tallmadge.

Polly answered. "Oh, yes. One of our men will go right to Oyster Bay and see my brother and tell him all this."

"Then there's nothing about the coach and your disappearance to connect matters with — with people who don't want to be connected with them?"

Polly shook her head vigorously. "Nothing."

"Then I'll see Caleb. Maybe in a day or two we can spirit you back to Oyster Bay. Does that sound reasonable?"

"I was just thinking, Major — it might be well if I didn't reappear too soon."

"Why?" asked Tallmadge, surprised.

Polly clasped her hands in front of her. "This is the way it seems to me. If I were kidnapped, I'd be held for ransom, wouldn't I? I know that's happened before and right close to Oyster Bay."

The major hesitated. "It's been known," he said.

"Then," Polly went on eagerly, "let Captain Brewster tell my brother to pretend to be negotiating for my safe return. The British won't interfere. So my return will seem much more natural if things drag out a little."

"By Jove, you're right," cried Grant.

Tallmadge looked at her quizzically. "Young lady, you have a most alert and far-ranging mind. I bow to it. Now let's see where you'd best stay."

"Why not right here?" said Grant, rising and leaning against the mantel.

Tallmadge seemed inwardly amused by something. "No," he said reluctantly, "too many odd fish drift in and out of Fairfield. My suggestion is that she go a little deeper upcountry."

"I don't see the need," said Grant stubbornly.

"You remember what started all this going?" said Tallmadge, raising his eyebrows. "A most dastardly letter, left in your room. If one such man came to Fairfield, another could. A charming young lady, held for ransom, would not be left in such an open port."

"I suppose not, said Grant grudgingly. "Then why not send her to the Hollis's? That's quite close and off the beaten track."

Tallmadge walked to the window and looked down across the Green. "No. Not to Mr. Hollis, I think."

"Why not?"

"It is, as you say, off the beaten track. But there's a constant coming and going of people, due to Mr. Hollis's position."

"Then where?" asked Grant.

Tallmadge seated himself beside Polly, "My dear, up in the hills lives an old veteran of the French Wars. An elderly housekeeper takes care of his big white house. It's on a ridge, a lovely spot. I know they'd be delighted to shelter you until it seems wise for you to attempt the crossing."

"Old Mr. Sammis!" cried Grant. "But, Lord, Major — way off there at Redding Ridge — "

"Away from what?" asked Tallmadge.

"Well, from the Sound and Captain Brewster's boats," said Grant.

Tallmadge smiled at Polly. "Miss Morgan, if you'll trust my judgment, you'll go inland. I'll send an escort of troopers with you and a note to Mr. Sammis. You should start as soon as possible. The less you're seen in Fairfield, especially in such dubious company, the better it will be."

Polly glanced at Grant, who said resignedly, "I'm afraid he's right."

She said quietly, "I'm sure you know best, Major. I'll go where-ever you wish."

Tallmadge beamed at her. "Fine. Now I'm off for Northcastle. Grant will have to stay here in command, as usual." He drew out a fat gold watch and looked at it. "I'll go below and speak to Moobie about your journey and order out the troopers. I wish you Godspeed, Miss Morgan." He caught up his helmet, bowed and strode out of the room.

"Well!" said Grant, watching the major's tall form disappear down the corridor."

Polly rose. "I suppose I'd better get my things. Mrs. Moobie is making up a packet for me."

"Ah — yes," said Grant. "You — you'll need things, I guess."

"She couldn't find much."

"I hope I'll see you when I come back from Redding Ridge, Grant."

Grant shifted his feet. "Oh, maybe I could manage to get up to Redding Ridge before it's time for you to go."

Polly gave a mechanical smile. "Maybe you could." She reached for her cloak.

"Let me help," said Grant. "Let's see." He was standing behind Polly, fingers fumbling with the cloak. Then his arms slid about her. She turned her face to him. Her voice was low and a little choked. "Oh, Grant!" she said. His lips met hers and the war and the treacherous Sound ceased to exist.

At last Grant whispered, "This is for good, Polly. It is for me, at any rate."

Her soft hair brushed Grant's forehead as she answered, "For me, too. It must be. Grant, I've only seen you twice in my life, but I know, inside me, that I love you very much. Those two times, with the stress and the crises they brought us are more like a span of years than days. I've come to know you so well and to love what I know."

Grant said huskily, "But that was what I was trying to say to you. In these times — "

"Dangerous times, Grant, and we've been through them together. We'll keep on, because we both believe in a cause that's bigger than either of us. I want to go on working with you, I want to be with you, forever."

"It is forever, Polly," said Grant. "It's more than I can put into words. But I can look way back to that first time we met and — "

He stepped hastily back as a heavy tread sounded on the stairs. From the doorway, Tallmadge surveyed them blandly. "The troopers are assembling now, Miss Morgan and I've found a good horse with a sidesaddle for you. Anything else?"

"Oh, I think not," replied Polly.

Tallmadge raised his eyebrows. "Sure?"

Grant spoke. "No. She isn't sure. What we both want is a chaplain, either to meet us at Redding Ridge or to be here when Polly comes back."

Polly came round the table and slipped her arm through Grant's.

"Captain Ledyard!" cried Tallmadge, striding forward and extending his hand. "My congratulations." The Major bowed to Polly. "My dear, heartiest good wishes — and with them the most regretful reminder that your escort is waiting. I'll see you below." He saluted and went out.

Grant caught Polly in his arms.

"Do be careful of yourself, Grant," she said. "You're mine as well as the country's now."

From the porch of the Oxbow, Grant watched them ride off. By the last turn, Polly twisted in her saddle and waved to him. Grant answered, bright helmet waving above his head. When the last trooper had vanished he walked slowly into the inn, a deep peace and joy in his heart.

As October deepened and the red and golds and oranges of the climbing hills to the north kindled, blazed, began to fade, Grant was aware of a cautious slackening about him. The armies were making ready for winter quarters. There would, of course, be swift, probing raids and exposed supply depots would be liable to attack. But no major move would be made until spring crept up from the South.

During the winter the secret road to New York must be kept open for intelligence from Culper and for inquiries from the Commander. There must be free travel over the Connecticut roads, where couriers from Rochambeau and from the Commander rode more frequently and more urgently. Grant ranged between the westernmost station at Stamford to New London in the east. Twice he crossed from Black Rock to the Setauket area where he met Austin Roe or Abraham Woodhull on the beaches.

At every pause in his journeying, Grant sent letters north to Redding Ridge by the post, by itinerant preachers, by passing carters. Polly wrote often. She told him she had been taken in as a daughter by old Mr. Sammis and his housekeeper. She seemed devoted to them. She missed Grant, she wrote. When would it be safe for her to return to Fairfield?

Grant read this after a night on Setauket beach and he wrote at once, ending:

> . . . our pack train friend tells me that the kidnaping story seems to be fully accepted, since such things have happened before. Your case, he thinks, should proceed like all the others. The Darnell girls and their brother (he says you'll know who they are) were spirited off and held for nearly two months before release was arranged. No need for us to wait that long, but he thinks now is a little soon. I'd like to come to Redding Ridge, but I am alone here in charge of the posts. Perhaps in a day or so —

An army surgeon, Danbury bound, provided quick means to start this letter on its way. Grant stood on the porch of the Oxbow giving the doctor final instructions for finding the Sammis house when he caught sight of a phaeton rolling slowly toward the Green from the Greenfield Hill road. When it came nearer he saw that Jethro Hollis was driving and Laurel was beside him. The phaeton stopped before one of the rebuilt houses and Hollis dropped to the ground. Laurel drove on calmly toward the inn.

Grant raised his helmet as Laurel pulled up. She smiled mischievously. "I expected you to ride up the valley to see us, Grant," she said.

"I've been busy, Laurel," he answered.

"I've wondered what kept you so busy, Grant," she remarked.

"I've men and horses to look after and feed, Laurel."

She frowned. "It makes me so impatient. You're wasting yourself on stable boy's work. You're doing nothing — even by your own lights. Grant — why don't you leave it?"

"Our country still needs me. I believe it's growing stronger," answered Grant.

"You mean it's going to batten on the French gold that's coming?" she asked sharply. "Your French friends are using that gold to pay you to kill Englishmen." Then after a moment she added, "Now you're hired soldiers — like those Germans whom the British pay to kill you." She looked keenly at him, then her voice changed. "Won't you come up the valley soon? We won't even mention the war."

Grant said politely, "My duties may bring me that way and I'd be glad to call."

She pressed her lips together. "I know your duties come first. But do ride by. We'd all be glad to see you." She flashed him a smile, raised her whip and rolled away.

Grant turned on his heel. "I'll be damned! If I can ride north, it'll be to Redding Ridge." Then suddenly he recalled Laurel's words. Did the French gold turn free Americans into mercenaries, hired to kill the enemies of France? Right now that kind of statement could be dangerous. If there were much talk like that about, it could have a very bad effect on the army. The French gold. He started up the stairs, then stopped again. She had said, "The French gold that's coming." What had she meant?

French gold had been sent from Newport to the army across the Hudson at Tappan. But she had spoken in the future — "the French gold that's coming." If more French gold were to be shipped west to the Commander, Grant would be one of the first to know of it, since he and his men would be put on the alert. Laurel must have meant gold already sent. He took off his helmet and jacket and stretched out on the bed for a little rest against his coming ride to Lyme to meet a French officer, bound for the Hudson.

Grant, with two troopers, escorted the Vicomte de Sergy from Lyme to Green Farms. The young Frenchman, quite fresh from the Court at Versailles, was agreeable enough but his outlook disturbed Grant. He was inclined to look on America and the war from an academic point of view, clinging to the theories that he had absorbed through reading. But when actuality ran counter to theory, he would say loftily, "Such is not the view of our Jean Jacques Rousseau." He told Grant with finality, "This town meeting of which you speak, *mon cher,* is the negation of freedom. It imposes its will on the Individual. You must read *Le Contrat Social.* Equality must be absolute."

Unwillingly Grant came to feel that if Rochambeau's army was officered by men like this who looked upon the American war as a laboratory wherein their theories could be proved, its participation could scarcely be wholehearted. From the vicomte's talk, Grant gathered that most of the French officers were not experienced soldiers but rather men who owed their military rank to their birth and their status at Versailles. How could such men face the tough, experienced British Army?

Also Grant had heard unpleasant mutterings from the troopers at various posts. The men were saying what Laurel had said, that free Americans were being bought by the French to fight the battles of His Most Christian Majesty, Louis XVI of France. Men were deserting because of such talk. Grant had to admit to himself that the present outlook was not bright. There was nothing left save the shrinking core of the Commander's army and the dubious assistance of the French.

Sergeant Graves, in charge during Grant's brief absence, brought in a few letters that had been delivered over to his care. Grant dismissed Graves and leafed through them.

He picked up one unmistakably addressed by the Commander himself. The Commander wanted immediate information, it seemed:

> Pray endeavour to secure intelligence whether any Works be thrown up on Harlem River, near to Harlem Town . . . what number of Men are kept therein . . . what Number and size Cannon . . . enquire if there be pits in front of such Works and if there be sharp, pointed Stakes therein fixed . . . the State of Forage and Fuel within the City of New York . . . the health and Spirits of Army, Navy and City . . .

He began to code rapidly on thin paper. From the Commander to Culper. That would be jlqn 711 vq 723; dated October 25, 1780 or 462-fk-enou. The jumble of letters and numbers grew. In a few days, no doubt, Rivington's *Gazette* would carry a paragraph telling of a picnic held along the banks of the Harlem River, those present including Captains This and That, Ensign This, Robert Townsend, Esquire, Mesdames . . . Later echoes of this picnic would cross Long Island, the Sound and finally be heard by the Commander in faraway Tappan.

Grant finished the letter, feeling a thrill of pride as he added his own number at the foot — 730. Yet his part was mere routine, that of a confidential clerk. The real risks, the real work were things in which he could only share vicariously. He folded the thin paper carefully, then ran over the other messages that held nothing of interest. He rose and looked out of the window.

He started to call for Sergeant Graves to take the coded letter to Brewster at Black Rock. Then he saw the two gangling Brimmer boys loping along a path that led down to the mouth of Ash-house Creek and the eastern beaches. Wind and tide were right and they were undoubtedly going to sail their battered little boat around Grover Hill to Black Rock where they kept their nets and lobster pots. Grant decided to go with them. A boat ride would save his horse and his own legs. It would take a little longer, but there was no hurry, for Caleb would not cross the Sound until sundown.

The boys eagerly made room for Grant and soon the little craft was heading east into a dark amethyst haze. Grant felt the crisp air in his face and was oddly content. There would be a profitable talk with Caleb, who would take the coded letter for transmission across to Setauket. Then he would either walk back to Fairfield or hail a chance-met wagon. By the time he returned to the Oxbow, there might be a letter from Polly.

The Brimmer boys brought their boat neatly into Black Rock. Grant sprang ashore, shouting, "Caleb!" Then he stopped, puzzled and a little alarmed. Infantrymen were standing in loose formation up by the sheds and warehouses. Their arms were neatly stacked and one of Caleb's men was addressing them. Caleb's flotilla, tied up at the waters, swarmed with more of his men who were coiling ropes, stowing water breakers and small kegs on board.

Caleb gave Grant a quick nod. "Expected you'd be along. Did you get my note?"

"Note? echoed Grant. "I've just come from the Oxbow. There was nothing from you."

Caleb looked disgusted. "That Noone! I sent him out with a note to you and a call for help to the nearest infantry. He's back so he must have forgotten about you. Don't matter. The infantry's here and there's nothing for you to do about all this. Just wanted you to know." He wiped his forehead. "We got word of a big raid planned by the folks across the Sound. They're going to hit up by New London." He licked his lips. "Grant, I'm going to catch them in the water with my swivel guns. I'll land my infantry to clean up any that manage to get ashore."

"Your information's sure?" asked Grant.

"The best," said Caleb grimly."

"In the meantime, can you send a message to the other side?" Caleb nodded reassuringly. "Sure. I'll send it after sundown."

Grant saw Caleb give the letter to a limping sergeant, dejected and morose because he was not included in the great coup at New London. For a while Grant watched the preparations, waiting until the whole flotilla moved out into the dusk of the Sound. Then he walked back to Fairfield.

There was still no letter from Polly at the Oxbow. Impatient and disgruntled, Grant ate a late supper and then sought his bed. For a while he tossed and turned, thinking of Caleb and his swift fleet cruising east along the Sound, its lookouts alert and the gunners ready to snatch the canvas jackets from the swivels in the bow. Then abruptly he fell asleep. Some hours later he woke, a feeling of pressure back of one ear and the smell of hot metal in his nostrils. He sat up with a start and a hand was removed from the back of his neck, transferred firmly to his mouth. The smell of hot metal persisted. Something clicked and rays from a dim lantern lighted for an instant the keen, sharp-featured face of Austin Roe.

Grant waited. Then he felt a gentle tug at his shoulder and the bedclothes were stripped back. Grant nodded in understanding and the hand was removed from across his mouth. He got out of bed and dressed in the dark. When he reached for jacket and helmet, the lantern flicked again and its rays fell on a broad hat, a dark cloak, a pair of light slippers.

He could hear Austin gently blow out the lantern, then a hand under his elbow guided him toward the door. In stocking feet the two crept down the stairs and out by a side door. They stopped to put on their shoes, and Austin led Grant down the path to the beaches. On they went in silence, Grant's apprehension growing with each step. His brain whirled with futile speculation. Something tremendous must have happened. Austin seemed to know the paths on the flats that led to the beach as well as Grant — or better. Twice he took sharp turns and once left the trail entirely to plow over sandy hillocks where the dry leaves of beach plums scratched against Grant's ankles. He heard the hiss and slap of water not far ahead, made out a ragged wall and recognized the ruins of the tide mill that the British had burned the year before. Austin reached back and caught Grant's wrist, guided him past the wall and into the remains of a shed.

"In here. I'll wait outside," he said in a low tone, and Grant entered the darkened shelter.

From the deepest shadow a voice spoke, calmly and pleasantly. "Good evening, Captain Ledyard. I hope you'll forgive our disturbing your slumbers."

Robert Townsend, Culper, 723, stood in the shelter of the ruined tide mill. Grant started, whispered hoarsely, "Good God! Townsend! What's happened! What are you doing here?"

"Easy now, Grant," Townsend answered calmly. "There's nothing to be alarmed about. Nothing's gone wrong. You've done a fine job here. Without your reports and letters, giving me such a fine picture of doings here, I should never have ventured this trip."

A sudden thought struck Grant. "You haven't been forced to leave New York, I hope."

"Thanks to you, no. I've seen and talked to General Arnold. I'm even writing a laudatory passage about him for Rivington, one that will be reprinted in London in the *Gentlemen's Magazine*." Grant caught the ghost of a chuckle as he went on, "I confess I find his inclusion in a gentlemen's magazine rather odd, but that's a thought I keep to myself in New York."

"Then you didn't have to come here?" There was wonder in Grant's voice.

Townsend went on. "Yes, I did have to come, on a matter of primary importance. French gold is being sent from Newport to our army. This is known in New York. So is the route. For the past few nights, people have been smuggled across the Sound, landing at various points. They will lie hidden in safe spots until the time to assemble. They've guides over here who know every inch of the country. They aim to intercept the French gold."

"Gold!" exclaimed Grant. "But that's all been sent."

"No," said Townsend, "this is a second shipment, larger than the first. It was supposed to be a great secret, but there was a leak somewhere."

"This is hard to believe," protested Grant. "Anything as important as this, I'd have to know about. So would Tallmadge."

Robert Townsend's breath went in sharply. "But Tallmadge does know!"

"He can't. He would have passed it on to me."

Townsend was silent for a moment, then went on in a troubled voice. "I don't like this, Ledyard. The matter was arranged between the Commander and Rochambeau. The Frenchman was to let the Commander know when the gold convoy started. Well, it *has* started, but Rochambeau's messengers can't have reached the Commander. Something's happened!"

"So it's up to us to see that the gold reaches the Commander," added Grant.

"Yes," said Townsend quietly. "The gold itself is valuable. But its safe arrival is far more important. The army has seen one shipment come in. Well and good. But they see a second and it will suggest to even the dullest that France is in earnest and behind us, that a constant stream may be expected. Ledyard, that gold has got to go through."

"You're right. But it'll surely be convoyed by our people. They'll be on the alert."

"That's just it," said Townsend. "The gold will start by pack horses from Newport, and the convoy's militia. It goes through Lebanon where the militia will fall out. Their places will be taken by some twenty troopers from Lauzun's Legion. These twenty French were to be met by double the number of our men just before they cross into Westchester, into the really dangerous country."

"That arrangement sounds safe enough to me," said Grant.

Townsend's voice rose. "But if the Commander doesn't know they've started, they won't be met. Worse still, the enemy may have united and will strike and start back for the coast before any help can come. We must smash the raiders as they re-embark. I think the point will be near Compo, and the loading should take a relatively long time so we have that one chance — "

Grant gave a low cry. "Caleb!" Fear swept over him.

"Caleb's the man," cried Townsend eagerly. "He must start at once — Every whaleboat, every swivel, every man."

Grant managed to say, "Caleb's gone."

After a moment Townsend said in an even, conversational tone, "Caleb's gone where?"

"To New London. He scraped up all the infantry he could and every whaleboat except one or two for messages. He had sure word of a raid in force. He left at sundown."

"Of course his information was false. There isn't any such raid," remarked Townsend. "It's all part of the same plan. The whole coast is stripped. Caleb's not to blame. I'm sure his news was most convincing. He's a very careful man."

Grant suddenly took courage from Townsend's calm acceptance of worse news added to bad. He said briskly, "All right. Then we'll just have to do what we can with what we have. First of all, I'll send a trooper to Tallmadge and Tallmadge will notify the Commander and do anything he can for us. I'll call in every man I can find and try to meet the convoy. That'll be a mighty thin chance, though."

"It may be that I can make it a little less thin for you. You see, I know their route and most important when and where the attack is supposed to take place. It will be tomorrow night at Redding Ridge."

"Redding Ridge? That's where we sent Polly!" cried Grant.

"Ah," said Townsend. "The devil! I knew you'd sent her inland. You never told me where. Who's seeing to her?"

"A Mr. Daniel Sammis."

Townsend gave a low whistle. "You know, you'll have to get word to her somehow. The gold's to lie over at that same house. The troopers will camp in the Sammis fields."

"We've got to get Polly out of there before anything happens."

"She will look after herself," Townsend said reassuringly. "The important thing is the gold."

"She has got to get out," Grant cried.

"Why so excited? I've known Polly for years. She'll be all right."

"Damn it, man, I'm going to marry Polly."

"Marry her! How delightful! My congratulations to both of you. This news is worth my whole trip. I'd say more but at the moment the gold's the important thing. You, Polly, and I — we simply do not count. For your part, it seems to me that your immediate goal must be the convoy. It'll cross the Housatonic at its junction with the Pomperaug, just north of Horse Hill."

"I know the route," said Grant. "I'll push right on until I find them."

"Capital!" said Townsend. "I must confess, my dear Ledyard, that I don't envy you the mission I've brought you: riding through the night to meet strangers for whom an ambush is planned. I simply couldn't face it."

"I'd take ten trips like this one rather than a minute of your time in Manhattan," Grant said soberly.

"Oh, but I'm wrapped in cloistered ease. Austin and I had better start for the other shore. Good-by and good luck, Grant. Ready, Austin?" They were at the door of the tide mill.

There was a final handclasp. Townsend and Roe slipped around a strip of wall, Grant followed them. He caught the glint of a narrow strip of water and the bulk of a waiting whaleboat. He watched the craft slide away into the night. Robert Townsend was returning to the delights of New York.

230

Grant hurried over the dark fields to the inn. He would send Sergeant Graves to Redding Ridge to warn Polly and Mr. Sammis. One trooper would go straight to Northcastle with word for Tallmadge. One must go east to alert the post at Stratford, while the remaining men routed out the staff at Green Farms and Stamford. He would set the rendezvous at the middle fork of Halfway River that flowed into the Housatonic.

French Gold

FAINT light was edging the crests of the highlands to the east of the Housatonic as Grant rode along the winding path that followed Toll Bridge Brook. At his left the brook gurgled cheerily and with the early dawn light he could see the white birches around it rustle and dip their bare branches. There was a new tang in the glass-clear air, a tang of wood smoke.

A challenge came sharp and sudden from the grove at his right. *"Qui vive?"* The convoy, well ahead of the schedule that Townsend had suggested, must have crossed the Housatonic before sundown. Grant answered, *"Ami! Officier! Dragons Américains!"* He halted and held his right hand high.

A short, stocky man in a fur busby and short cavalry jacket stepped into sight, a light carbine held at ready. In the half-light he surveyed Grant critically. Then he lowered his carbine, *"Bon! Monsieur l'officier désire?"*

Grant dismounted. *"Le chevalier d'Ostel."*

The guard took Grant's bridle. *"Par ici."*

The way led into a natural amphitheater. As Grant looked about him, his professional spirits rose. The camp was trim and soldierly. The horses were staked out in an even line and guards watched at both ends. Farther in, more horses had pack saddles neatly ranged beside them and, barely visible among some rocks were stacks of small, oblong boxes that must have held the French gold. On a long stretch of fallen leaves, men slept in orderly rows, their equipment at their feet, and an eight-foot lance towered above each head, its point driven into the ground, an exotic weapon for North America.

The chevalier might be fresh from Versailles, Grant thought, but he certainly had some seasoned noncoms who knew their trade.

A tall, lean man was walking toward the trooper who led Grant's horse. He wore a shapeless felt hat, a fringed hunting shirt and loose leather breeches tucked into battered boots. As he came closer, Grant saw that he limped slightly and had a craggy, clean-shaven face that stood out oddly among the fierce mustaches of the troopers. Grant's guide saluted the man, who asked in a deep voice, *"Que voulez-vous, mon enfant?"* There was a brief exchange of sentences while Grant stared in amazement. Then the tall man approached him.

"I am d'Ostel," he said in French. "May I be of service to you?"

Grant explained rapidly what he had learned of the ambush and the steps which he himself had taken. The chevalier nodded and his dark brown eyes took on a cold glint. "Ah, yes," he said. "In war, such things happen. So no troops meet us? Then we must take other steps. How many sabers do you count on joining us?"

"Seven at the most."

"Allons," observed d'Ostel agreeably. "Matters do not march so badly. Seven sabers, not counting your own, added to my twenty lances."

"We still have to reckon on some fifty of the enemy, perhaps more."

"No doubt."

"You don't seem disturbed, Captain."

D'Ostel shrugged. "Boldness is our best course. I feel that we should not alter our route. You share my opinion?"

"I'd like to change the route, but I don't dare," said Grant. "Swinging up to the north would take too long. The coast road is too exposed. When do you want to start?"

"My orders call for a long rest here, but I suggest that we push on at once, thus arriving sooner than our enemies expect. Let's take coffee and a crust of bread and set off."

Coffee and bread were quickly finished. The little column started out, lances bristling on either side of the pack horses which were carrying their gold. Grant chafed at the slow progress. He turned to d'Ostel. "I'd be glad, Captain, if we could hit a quicker pace."

D'Ostel looked surprised. "But my friend, even at a snail's gait, we reach your Redding Ridge hours before we are expected."

"That may be. But, damn it, I want to get on. You see, my fiancée is up there."

"*Sapristi*. I did not know," exclaimed d'Ostel. "But figure to yourself, important as she is, our first charge is the gold. Spent men and foundered horses make a poor guard for it."

"But if — oh, the devil. You're right of course," said Grant resignedly.

The cortege clanked on through the Connecticut morning. At Grant's side d'Ostel talked now in French, now switching into English. "This all must be a great change for you," Grant said to the Frenchman, "this new world and the new life."

D'Ostel gave a short laugh. "Ah, I believe you, it is a change. Our last service was in Senegal, a country of swamps, fevers and murderous blacks, on the extreme western tip of Africa. Yes, Connecticut is different. Now yourself — *Holà!* What is that?"

They had reached the middle-fork of Halfway River where four troopers of the 2nd Continental Dragoons were waiting patiently. Grant said casually, "A few of my lads. I judged it advisable to have them here to meet us." Inwardly, he swelled with pride. His men, like seasoned troopers, had taken advantage of their halt to loosen girths and slip bridles. Now, a few hundred yards away, Grant could see them cinching up, adjusting bits and then mounting, hurried but efficient. His pride increased as they trotted toward him, their horses were well-groomed and their uniforms trim.

Lean Sergeant Turner, from Green Farms, saluted smartly as he halted his small, primed detail. Grant was aware of a stir among d'Ostel's men. A gratifying murmur of approval met his ears. Grant nodded to Turner. "Good work. I want you and your men to cover the right flank. Keep to the ridges when we're in the hollows and fan out when we're in the plains." Turner and his squad cantered off.

Held back by the laden pack horses, the column wound slowly on through the crisp fall air. By noon Grant judged, it would be struggling up the killing S curve that led from the Aspetuck west to Redding Ridge. "We're a good many hours ahead of schedule," he remarked.

"And each one adds to our strength," replied d'Ostel. "But, *mon ami,* our greatest strength lies in the fact that the Messieurs, our enemies, do not know that we are aware of the ambush. By the way, you have not told me how you learned of it. Naturally, one is curious."

"Word was brought me from across the Sound by a man who calls himself timid."

"Ah!" exclaimed d'Ostel. "That sort of timidity, I envy. I stand in awe and reverence. We others, with our noise and our trumpets and banners are all very well, but those like your timid friend who work in a world of dead silence — *ah çà* — before such we may only bow. Now, with your leave, we halt to rest the pack horses."

"Halt again?" asked Grant. "Still, I suppose the beasts will be better for a rest. Look here — this road runs straight to the Ridge. No turn-offs. I'm going to ride on ahead. I am anxious to see my fiancée, as I have told you. It won't do any harm for me to have a look at the countryside ahead of you."

D'Ostel clapped him on the shoulder, laughing. "By all means, *mon ami.* Reconnoiter ahead of us — and my respects to Mademoiselle."

The morning grew brighter as Grant rode on. Partridges whirred up from clumps of birches and once he sighted a fox, red and glistening in the sunlight. A few more twists, a couple of deceptive level stretches and he would be at the top. He would ride in with a great clatter and shout and surprise Polly.

On the crest at last, he turned, set out at a gallop for the Sammis house. As he approached he saw that horses were tethered in front of the barn. There must be guests. He pulled up by the low, pillared porch, vaulted to the ground, calling, "Polly!" The house stood silent. He called again, "Polly! Where are you?"

The door rattled, then slowly swung open and Grant gave a start. "Why Grant! What brings you here?" asked Laurel Dane.

He stared, then managed to say, "How pleasant — and unexpected. What brings *you* here?"

Laurel was pale. Her riding habit of dark green was mud-splashed. "Why — why I came here with Uncle Jethro. He has business with Mr. Sammis. Won't you come in?"

Grant dropped his reins over the hitching post by the door. "Thank you." He started to say, "Where's Miss Morgan?" but checked himself on some obscure impulse, and asked about Mr. Sammis instead.

As he entered, Laurel answered, "He's gone up the road to Sunset Hill with Uncle Jethro. His housekeeper's gone, too." Laurel seated herself on a fragile chair in the front room while Grant sat opposite her. There was a suppressed excitement in her eyes and once or twice he thought he saw color start to flood into her cheeks again.

"You're still working for the destitute families?" he asked.

"Well, mostly," said Laurel. Her eyes kept darting toward the hall and the room beyond where windows looked out to the front of the barn.

"What's the matter with her?" thought Grant.

Laurel suddenly rose with a nervous motion and stood with her head cocked toward the stable. Grant heard muffled sounds as though people were scuffling somewhere in the house. There was a sudden thin sound that might have been a high-pitched laugh, a distant clatter of boots.

Laurel said suddenly, "Will you excuse me for a moment?"

Grant rose. "Can I help?"

But Laurel had glided through the door. To Grant's amazement, she slammed it behind her, the hollow boom almost hiding the sharp click as the key turned on the far side.

He stood staring at the white panels. He shook at the pine door, but the frame held firm. Once again he shook it, then drove his shoulder against it. There was a quick grinding sound. The key, only partly turned, had slipped around. Grant flung open the door, saw that the little hall was empty. Darting into the room opposite, he rushed to the window.

Out by the front of the barn, the Sammis stableboy, was vaulting onto one of the tethered horses, working frantically at the halter knot. The knot gave and the boys swung the horse's head along the curving drive toward the road.

The whole scene was incomprehensible. Dimly he heard Laurel's voice — a new, harsh voice. "Mike! George! After him! Don't let him get away!" Then Laurel moved into view just as the stableboy made the turn toward the road. Her hands were busy under her cloak, then a pistol glittered in her hand, shot out smoke and a stab of flame. Other shots flashed from bushes closer to the drive. The boy lurched forward over the horse's neck and fell. His body jolted over the hard surface, one foot caught in a stirrup. Out in the drive Laurel cooly stowed away her pistol. Without turning her head she called in a high, shrill voice, "Get that body out of sight. Tether his horse with the others!"

Grant was stunned and incredulous. He recognized that voice — the girl's voice in the ravine! So it was Laurel — Laurel who had been with the men who attacked him. Laurel, who had said she hated violence and war, had been with those men, directing them, inciting them. Grant gripped the window casing until his knuckles were white. He saw two burly men bend over the body of the stableboy.

He shook his head in bewilderment. What was going on here? Where was Polly? Where was Mr. Sammis? Grant ran to the other window which looked north onto the highway. He saw two horses jogging south, shoulder to shoulder. The nearer was ridden by a

237

powerfully built man whose uniform was unknown to Grant. It might have been that of any militia company, perhaps of some Tory levy. On the other horse, somber and decorous, almost Quakerlike, Jethro Hollis paced unobtrusively along, nodding his head from time to time. Hollis must have had some news of the attack on the gold. Just how was he connected with it? Grant flung open the window, shouted, "Mr. Hollis!"

The assemblyman gave a visible start, peered hastily past his uniformed companions. Grant called again. "Just a minute. I'll be right out." He backed away from the window into something that bored into his ribs. A harsh voice said, "Keep right on looking at the road." Gnarled hands reached out and unbuckled his sword. Then the hands slapped at his breeches, his coat and the voice grunted, "He's clean. Not a toothpick on him. Turn around. Hands high."

Mechanically Grant turned. A lean, rangy civilian held two pistols level with the middle button of Grant's waistcoat. Beyond him, another man chuckled gloatingly, "God, what a soldier! A baby could have took him."

Grant eyed the pair covertly, while his mind whirled as he tried to link up their presence with that of Laurel and her uncle. Then Laurel stepped into the room. The eyes that Grant had so often seen cloud over at any mention of the war, eyes that had filled when she spoke of the sufferings of people through that war, were hard and cold as they met his. She spoke crisply to him. "You're in the way. Don't start wondering how you can interfere. We won't allow it."

Full knowledge struck Grant. So it was true that Laurel had been playing a part. And if Laurel, then Rosa too. And if Rosa — Jethro Hollis who sat with the Assembly. He glanced quickly at Laurel who was looking bitterly at him. He felt perspiration start under his helmet, trickle down his forehead. How much had she found out about his real work at Fairfield? About Tallmadge, Brewster? Utterly unsuspecting, what had he let drop in talking to her? She, Rosa and Hollis — that explained the leak! The intelligence that had been sifting steadily through Fairfield and Westchester Counties to Manhattan. Rallying himself he managed an awkward bow without dropping his hands. "My congratulations, Laurel. I was completely fooled."

"Of course," said Laurel tersely. "It wasn't hard. I thought for a while you'd be worth watching. It didn't seem possible that even your army would be stupid enough to keep you doing sergeant's work with your little cavalry posts." She gave a dry laugh. "If you'd been doing more than that, I assure you that we could have stopped you — at any time."

"Perhaps," said Grant.

"Anyway," said Laurel, "you'll have to go to the hulks. We've ways of getting you across the Sound. Yes, the hulks, if you're lucky. You won't travel alone, either."

Grant started. "Polly! Where is she? If you've harmed her — "

Laurel smiled again. "Don't worry about your little protégée. She's quite safe with us. And don't you think that you can do anything. You're in our hands as surely as though you were in Manhattan. You and she. Now you men, take him to the salt-box house. Tie him up and stay with him. I'll send you word about him later."

Grant was shoved out of a side door. In a small shed beyond the house, a packing case stood open, the sun striking down on the white crests and bright metal of helmets much like those of the 2nd Dragoons. Those helmets must have been worn by the men who burned out the Hiltons, to make the outrage seem as though it had been done by American troops. Now, surely those same helmets would be worn by some of the men in the ambush of the convoy and the French would think the Commander's troops to be mere banditti.

The convoy! Grant purposely dragged his feet. Hollis, Laurel and the others still thought that the pack horses would not arrive till sundown. They could not know that d'Ostel and his lancers were nearing the ridge. Suddenly the pressure of the pistols at his back eased a little. One of his guards shouted, "Holy Timothy, Mike. Look at that!"

The pressure was gone. Grant turned, saw both his guards starting back toward the house. Hollis was mounting hurriedly and the man in the strange uniform was already in the saddle. Laurel pulled in between them on a small black horse. The mounts milled for a moment, then all three shot away west along the road that led to Ridgefield. With a drumming of hoofs, other men appeared from the direction of the barn, followed them. One guard croaked, "Suffering Moses, they ain't leaving *me* behind!" and began to run. The other hesitated, then started after him. Grant gave a sudden lunge, snapped his arms about the man's knees and threw him heavily. The guard's breath went out in a great gasp and Grant snatched up the pistol and pressed it against his shoulders. "Quick now. Where's the girl?"

His opponent writhed under him. "Don't know. Let me up."

Grant slipped his free hand under the other's chin, while his knees pressed hard against the small of his enemy's back. Grant gave a wrench, forcing the stubbly chin around. There was a strangled croak, "God! You're killing me."

"Where is she?" snapped Grant with another wrench.

The man went limp, his voice a thick gurgle. "To the cider mill."

"Where's that?"

"Along the hill, back of the salt box. God almighty, let me up."

Grant got to his feet, panting. The man scrambled up and raced toward the Sammis house. Grant shouted a warning, then lowered his pistol with a grim smile. He saw the reason for the hasty departure of Laurel and the others. Turner and one dragoon were in sight by the porch. Beyond them, bright against the stark trees, lance points gleamed and the sun caught the sheen of fur busbies. The convoy had arrived. The guard would not run far.

Grant stowed away his pistol, turned on his heel and hurried along the hillside where pumpkins glowed among neatly shucked cornstalks. There, off to the left, was the sloping roof of the salt box. Then he caught sight of the solid little cider mill, built into the hill. He pulled at the door, flung it open and shouted, "Polly! Polly!" Dark hair streaming and eyes aglow, Polly ran to him, her feet skimming over the rough boards. Grant caught her in mid-flight, lifted her clear of the floor. "Polly!" he cried again. "Are you all right?" Arms about his neck she said, "I prayed that you would come. Oh, Grant, you've got to do something! The French gold, I've heard them talking about it! Rosa says —"

Grant glowered at Rosa Hollis who sat white-faced on a stool beyond the press. "Never mind about Rosa," he said grimly. "We'll see to her."

"You don't understand. Rosa isn't with those others. She's had a terrible shock. She just found out about them. They tied her up with me. She rode in just a little while after they did!"

"It's a trick of some kind," said Grant shortly. "These people are slippery fish."

Polly shook his arm gently. "Grant, I *know!* I saw it all. She's sick with the shock. Her own father! Grant, help her. I swear she's sterling."

Grant walked over to Rosa who sat with her green eyes on the ground. In a faint voice she said, "You'll never believe me. I don't blame you." Her hands were trembling. "You'll arrest me. I don't care what happens — now."

Grant looked at her sagging shoulders, the bowed head, and knew that Polly was right. He said gently, "Rosa, I believe you."

As though she hadn't heard him, Rosa went on, "I've been so blind. I ought to have known, with all those horses in the stables and people riding up at all hours. I ought to have known that no-body could have been what Laurel pretended to be. But everything seemed such fun, riding over the country and watching soldiers on the march and boats leaving Black Rock. I must have told them a lot that they wanted to know. And poor Aunt Ann. She suspected as little as I did. This will be an awful blow to her."

"No harm done," said Grant soothingly. "Where's Mr. Sammis?"

"They were tricked into going up to Litchfield," Rosa answered wearily.

Polly put an arm about her. "Now, Grant, we've got to do something about the French and their gold."

Grant smiled at her. "That's all been done. The convoy's here. The others have gone, very hastily. Oh, yes, we know about the ambush. We got word."

"From — ?" Polly tilted her head south.

"Exactly. Now you both had better come to the house with me." He touched some frayed cords on the floor. "You said you were tied up. How did you get free."

"Polly did it," said Rosa. "She bit through my bonds and then I untied her."

Grant held the door open for the girls and then followed them out into the clear day. Up by the house he could see d'Ostel and Turner talking with a man in civilian clothes. The lancers had snapped up at least one of his guards, who seemed to be talking eagerly as he stood between a French lancer and an American dragoon. Grant shouted and d'Ostel came hurrying toward him, leaving the prisoner to Turner.

"Is this your guide?" asked Polly, eying the fringed shirt and battered hat.

"The very best guide we could hope for," answered Grant. "May I present Captain le Chevalier d'Ostel of Lauzun's Legion? Miss Morgan, Miss Hollis."

D'Ostel swept off his old hat and for an instant it seemed topped with flowing plumes and the stained hunting shirt gay with arabesques of silver braid. "It is I who am enchanted," he said to Polly. "Captain Ledyard, my felicitations." He turned to Rosa, "Your devoted servant, mademoiselle."

"You have a sharp eye, d'Ostel," laughed Grant. "How did you know which was which?"

"Ah, how indeed!" echoed d'Ostel. "Now tell me, *mon ami,* there has been some slight contretemps here?"

"I was ambushed by some of the ringleaders. They seem to have left rather hurriedly," answered Grant.

"They left very quickly, even to the point of abandoning not only your horse but your saber. My little rascals saw two flying afoot and seized them. They now answer the questions of your Sergeant Turner. They say the attack was planned for sundown when it was hoped that we might be caught strung out like a chain of sausages along that devil of a hill."

"That's right," said Rosa. "I heard that much, anyway."

"So our next question is what to do," observed Grant. "Shall we await the attack here or push on west?"

D'Ostel turned to Rosa. "Did you hear anything else that might guide our choice, mademoiselle?"

Rosa said hesitantly, "Their force is scattered in little groups to the west, north and south." She looked up at Grant. "That's true. You've got to believe me."

"We do, Rosa," said Grant quickly. "I think that answers our questions, Chevalier. If we go west, we'll be strung out along the road in the place where they'll be thickest."

"Agreed," said d'Ostel. "Then I say that we turn this charming white house into a fortress and stand siege."

Polly looked inquiringly at him. "For how long?"

"I sent word to Tallmadge about all this," put in Grant. "He'll bring on his dragoons."

Rosa shook her head wearily. "*If* your messenger got through. Last night they were stopping everyone abroad on the roads."

"In that case," said d'Ostel, "we hold our fort, *tout simple. Allons,* let us go to our towers and battlements." He offered Rosa his arm and started for the house, Grant and Polly following.

Polly asked, "Where did you ever meet that Dane girl? I never heard you speak of her."

Grant told of crossing the Sound with Laurel and her aunt. "I kept running into her after we got to Fairfield. She pretended to hate war and was always trying to get me to leave the army. I suppose she thought that even if she detached one experienced officer from the forces, it would be worth while along with her other work. She may have tried the same thing on others. I don't know."

Polly gently pulled at his arm. "That's all past, Grant. Come on. Let's get to the house. Tell me, are you really worried about this siege?"

"I'm worried about you, Polly. We'll have to find a safe spot for you. As for the rest, the military side, I'm not too greatly troubled." He wondered if she believed his last sentence.

Dragoons and lancers were busy as he and Polly reached the porch. The horses were being driven into a wide cattle pen between the barn and the rear of the house. Inside, men were piling the gold chests against the windows of the southwest front room. In other parts of the house, the sound of hatchets echoed as loopholes were cut in the heavy wooden shutters. Two lancers clumped into the house carrying slopping water buckets in case of fire. At the door, d'Ostel handed Grant his saber and his double-barreled pistols.

"We have to assume that my message got through to Tallmadge," Grant said. "We must assume, too, that the enemy is mustering his scattered forces at this moment. We can't be caught off guard, so, if it suits you, we'd better send out patrols to watch. One lancer and one dragoon to the north, the same to the west and the south."

"*Parfaitement,*" said d'Ostel. "And one of my men shall climb that great elm by the front door."

The patrols were sent out and a squat little trooper scrambled nimbly into the topmost branches of the elm. "Now what?" asked Grant.

"Now?" asked d'Ostel. "But what else than this?" He shouted, "*Allons, mes enfants, la soupe!*"

There was a thick, fragrant stew, strong black coffee and slabs of tough-crusted bread. Grant and Polly sat on the steps of the porch, eating from bowls that Rosa brought from the Sammis kitchen. Polly looked west. "That's the way they'll come, isn't it? Mostly from the west, I mean?"

Grant nodded. "It's what I'd do if I were running them."

"Then they'll have a very strong sun at their backs and we'll have it in our eyes." She kept looking west, her chin in her hand.

"Do you see something?" Grant asked, noticing her absorption.

She turned to him. "This is all so peaceful. It's hard to realize that the peace is false, that people are massing somewhere off there, coming against us."

The autumn hush deepened. A few chickadees hopped through the leafless bushes, twittering their joy over bits of crust that Polly tossed them. Inside the house, voices buzzed with a deceptive sleepiness, and from the pens, horses whinnied. Somewhere near the stables, a man was singing in a high, wailing minor:

> *Mon mari, il est parti*
> *A la guerre d'Espagne —*

Time ebbed gently on, and the sun sank lower and lower toward the west. High up in the great elm, a shrill whistle rang out. Grant and d'Ostel sprang up as the man in the tree slithered down to the lowest fork and held his arm crooked across his forehead. "To the north, *mon capitaine,*" he called.

"What is it?" asked Polly, on her feet at once.

"He must have seen the north patrol," said Grant. "Let's get out in the road."

D'Ostel was there before them, staring up the long, brown track that led to Sunset Hill. "Ah!" cried Polly.

Silhouetted against the deep blue of the sky, two horsemen stood broadside to the road, turned toward the north. As though a spring had been touched, both riders wheeled, started down the slope toward the Sammis house at a gallop, the dragoon turning in his saddle to loose off a shot. Hardly had the echoes died when a second carbine cracked off to the west, then one to the south and the wind carried a quickening drum of hoofs.

245

Grant saw Rosa look at d'Ostel, who nodded. "The pot begins to boil," he said.

Grant shouted, "Under cover, everyone. Polly, you and Rosa had better go into that little inner room between the kitchen and the dining room." He took her hands. "It'll be perfectly safe."

She turned quickly. "Come along Rosa."

"Lead the way, Polly," she replied. "We'll find something we can do to help."

They vanished through the door and Grant went farther out in the road, waiting with d'Ostel for the arrival of the patrol from the north. Dragoon and lancer clattered to a halt and dismounted. The dragoon saluted Grant. "Nigh to thirty men, maybe more. Most on foot and headed this way."

The other patrols galloped up, reported even larger bodies approaching. "Ninety to a hundred against us," said Grant to d'Ostel.

"As I observed, the pot boils," said d'Ostel. "At least, there is an end to waiting."

Sergeant Turner came up panting. "More dragoons, sir. The south patrol met them."

Grant's hopes soared. "From Major Tallmadge?"

"No, sir. The Stamford post and two men who'd been on leave."

"Better than nothing," said Grant disappointed. "Turn all horses into the pen and send your troopers to the second floor. Now, d'Ostel, you've got more men than I, so you're in command. I'm going up to the porch roof, with your leave, and watch from there. Turner knows that he and his men take orders from you."

He went into the house, and mounted to the second floor where dragoons and lancers were peering out through their crude loopholes. Pistols and carbines were neatly arranged on the floor near the windows and some resourceful soul had rummaged through the Sammis closets and found two old muskets and four fowling pieces.

He flung open the shutter and climbed out onto the gentle slope of the porch roof. North, south and west, the roads were still empty.

Those to the east could be forgotten since that face of the ridge was far too open for an avenue of attack. But somewhere out of sight, the leaders of the three converging forces were conferring, arguing, altering their plans. Their main concern, Grant reasoned, would be to strike quickly, secure their booty and fall back toward the Sound, a pretty safe route for them since that whole area had been stripped of troops by Caleb's false move to New London.

XII

Rescue

THERE was movement on the long slope of Sunset Hill to the
north. A loose, drab column of men was moving down it and the
sun picked out the bright glint of bayonets. West across the long
flat of the ridge, more men appeared. The enemy came on in a
sullen flow, the head of the western column about a quarter of a
mile away. "Blast them," muttered Grant. "They've chosen the
best time to attack." The sinking sun turned the west into a blinding glare of red that blurred the whole scene. He turned to the
lancers and dragoons behind him, but there was no need to warn
them. In that room, in the one beyond, from an attic window under
the north gable, from the ground floor, he heard shouts. "Here
they come!" . . . *"En garde!"* . . . *"En vue!"* . . . "Look to your
priming!" Grant re-entered the room and went downstairs, where
he found d'Ostel pacing up and down. There was a lancer at each
loophole, an eight-foot spear leaning against the wall beside him.
D'Ostel nodded. "In case of a melee at close quarters, lacking
bayonets, these lances will serve."

Somewhere in the house, broken glass tinkled. A man yelped in
pain, cried, *"Aïe! Ça chauffe!"*

"What the devil?" cried Grant, running toward the sound.

In the inner room Polly and Rosa bent over a table where two
lamps burned, heavy, choking black smoke rolling from the wicks.
With a small pair of tongs, Rosa was holding a jagged strip of glass
in the smoke and Polly was just reaching for another. Just beyond
Rosa, a small lancer danced up and down, his fingers in his mouth.
Without looking up, Polly cried, "Wait till it cools. Here, Rosa,

248

that one's smoked enough. Put it on the edge of the table!" As she reached her tongs for a fresh piece of glass she saw Grant. "Oh there you are!" She flicked a tentative finger at a blackened glass fragment, handed it to the dragoon. "That's cool enough now. Better take these to your friends." She pushed a few more strips into his hands and he slipped away with a bow.

"What on earth are you doing here?" asked Grant.

"Smoking glass. One man holds it over the loophole for the man who's firing. Take a piece. It really works."

Grant bent, kissed her and strode out. Turner and his men were eagerly peering through the loopholes, muttering in satisfaction as the sooty bits of glass they held melted down the glare of the sun.

Without looking around, Turner said, "Seems like they can't make up their minds." He stepped aside and Grant took his place, smoked glass before his eyes.

The western fields were swarming with men who moved uncertainly. More were pouring down from the north, leaving the road and fanning out. Here and there he made out uniformed men who seemed to be acting like sheep dogs for the rest, waving them, pulling them, butting them into some kind of order. Behind the confused mass were a pair of low carts heaped with objects that he couldn't distinguish and near the carts, a few figures on horseback. The wind freshened and he caught the flutter of a skirt, the flick of a cape. Laurel was out there, watching. Beside her Jethro Hollis's unmartial bulk was obvious.

A hush fell over the fields. Jethro Hollis's uniformed companion rode forward, raised his hand, dropped it. From the far right and the far left, musket shots rang out and the whole ragged line swayed forward. Grant looked over his shoulder, shouting, "Steady! Not yet!" More shots from outside and a few bullets rapped harmlessly against the side of the house. From below he heard d'Ostel call calmly, *"Doucement, mes enfants."*

The thick, drab line halted clumsily. Then its center shook and a compact body of men, heads down and legs churning, dashed onto the road, crossed it, stormed toward the house. The main body stirred, moved nearer; a ripple of flashes ran along it, died away in thick smoke, was renewed.

The men at the loopholes grew suddenly tense, tightened their fingers on the triggers of pistols and carbines. An odd, flat chattering filled the house. The men were concentrating on the storming party, not wasting their shots on the more distant line that was keeping up its covering fire. Down on the lawn, men pitched and stumbled, fell with upflung arms, leaving a trail of brownish forms from the road to the dead space under the porch roof.

Below, the din kept up. Feet pounded on the boards of the porch and musket butts jarred against the front door. The firing died away below him. There was a heavy rasping noise and d'Ostel's roar carried clear and sharp to Grant. *"En avant! Pointez!"* A tangle of struggling forms showed on the grass below. D'Ostel had thrown half a dozen of his lancers among the attackers. Men threw up their muskets to parry the slick, deadly thrust of the lances, stood back to back trying vainly to fence against this unorthodox sortie. Two fell, then a third, and fourth. The rest fled, and the lancers returned to the house.

Carbine butts thumped on the floor below him, rammers slid through barrels with a whining sound. Grant heard Polly's clear voice. "Tear up that sheet, Rosa. It went right through his shoulder." So one of the garrison was wounded. Then a dragging, bumping noise told Grant that still another had been hit. He called down the stairs to d'Ostel, "What losses?"

"Two killed, two wounded. Ah, we were lucky, I assure you," answered d'Ostel.

Polly appeared at the foot of the stairs. "We're all right, Grant. We're looking after the wounded."

Relieved, Grant went into the front room again. A lancer yelled, fired through his loophole.

A heavy burst of musketry from the western fields followed the lancer's shot. Grant ran to a loophole. Bullets were rapping thicker against the walls. Two struck close by his shutter and fine splinters stung his face. A dragoon backed away from his post with a graceful, gliding step and sank slowly to the floor. "Look to him!" called Grant without taking his eyes from his loophole.

The attacking lines had come closer out of the sunset and Grant estimated their strength at over a hundred. From the garret above, a man yelled, "Look out! They're coming in from the north!" Grant swore under his breath. More men! Robert Townsend's original count of fifty-odd had been very short. From below, d'Ostel shouted a warning of still more men from the south. Once again the firing died away.

D'Ostel appeared in the doorway. "Frankly, *mon ami,* I do not like the way matters arrange themselves. This burst of fire, the attackers waiting and this hush. Another fact which puzzles me is that they do not yet annoy our horses."

"Of course not," said Grant. "They want to use them themselves. How are the girls?"

"Ah, but they comport themselves magnificently," cried d'Ostel. "They do much for our men. They have wise heads, those demoiselles." D'Ostel held up his hand as musketry rattled out in the fields. "The music begins again." He dropped down the stairs and Grant went back to his post.

The sun dipped below the horizon and the men tossed aside their bits of smoked glass. Out in the fields there was an ominous stir. The treble line looked more solid, better ordered. Through the dusk that was gathering in the west, two carts lumbered over the rough ground, halted. Men scrambled into them, began unloading heavy logs. Behind the carts Grant saw Laurel and Hollis, the former making quick, urgent gestures to the men. Groups of six and eight heaved the logs to their shoulders and stood waiting. "Battering rams!" Grant said through his teeth.

A man in green and blue was walking along the front of the line, apparently issuing orders. Then he blew a whistle. North, west and south, musketry blasted out. There was no blind rush this time. Steadily and methodically the bulk of the line fired on the shuttered windows of the house. Other men threw themselves flat, worked cautiously forward across the road, taking full advantage of tree, hedge and bush. Grant ran to the north window just in time to catch the body of the lancer who had been guarding it. He laid the man aside gently, then looked out. Some thirty men, vaguely outlined in the failing light, were lying in the grass and keeping up a steady drum of fire. Others behind them passed up loaded muskets, took the empty ones. They showed no tendency to advance.

The whistle blew again. It was answered by a shout. The groups of men carrying the logs moved forward at a clumsy trot and those on the lawn sprang to their feet, ducking low to avoid the fire from the loopholes. One of the log men was down, a whole group was down. Another log rolled in the road. There was a heavy crash below. One log, two logs had reached the door. Grant yelled, "To the stairs!" and went down, two at a time. As he reached the front hall he saw the great door shiver, saw a clean white splinter drop from it. He drew his pistols, yelling, "The girls, d'Ostel."

From the murk of the gold room, d'Ostel tottered out, balanced, then fell across Grant's feet, the back of his worn hunting shirt slowly staining, wetly red. Just then a dragoon backed into the room, shouting, "They've staved it in — there goes a box!" He dashed out again.

Grant stepped across d'Ostel and followed the dragoon into the room where the gold was stored. In the powder smoke, men struggled. A gaping hole showed where one set of shutters had been battered away. A long hooked pole reached into the hole and wrenched one of the boxes out into the night. Grant raised a pistol, loosed a barrel out into the dusk, poised for a second shot. A hand clawed at his shoulder and spun him about. Pale under his powder stains, Turner yelled, "It's all over. The east fields are thick with 'em, heading here fast. They're closing in on the horses!"

"Then we'll meet 'em here," shouted Grant. "Every man that can stand! *Holà, les lanciers!* Dragoons, on your feet! This way, the 2nd!"

The logs still thundered at the door and out of the corner of his eye he saw the hook pole rise again. The door bulged inward and he fired once, twice at a yawning gap and heard a heavy crash outside. A lancer fired over his shoulder at the door. Blindly, Grant whirled about, started for the back of the house. "Polly! Rosa! Where are you?"

Strangely the firing outside was dying away as though a door were closing on it. High and clear in the west, out of the dusk, a cavalry bugle sang, mingled with sudden yells of panic. There were drumming feet on the porch, an endless thumping and thudding over the grass all about the house, as though the coming night were alive with running feet. The bugle sang out again.

Grant lunged toward the shattered door, tossed aside the heavy oak bar that secured it and flung it open. The fields to the west and south were thick with fleeing men; among them bright streaks swooped and darted like fireflies as the evening glow picked out silver helmets and the flicker of sabers. Grant raced out onto the road shouting, 'The 2nd! Swing to the east! Fresh troops there!" As he called, a voice behind him panted, "Never mind the east. It was us." A very young ensign, excited eyes dancing under the crested light infantry cap of the Continental Line, stood beside Grant. "It was us. He slipped us around and — "

Grant could only stand, pistols dangling from his hands and stare first at the swarming fields and then at the quick-footed light infantry who filtered up past the house and formed into line on the road. Chest heaving, he muttered, "Just in time." Then hoofs pounded up the drive and he cried out in surprise and relief. D'Ostel, naked to the waist save for a dark-stained bandage that cut across from waist to shoulder, galloped onto the road, sword drawn and a dozen lancers riding hard behind him. His shout, *"Pointez, lanciers! Pointez!"* echoed through the dusk as he swung his men out to join the 2nd Dragoons in the pursuit.

Voices cried, "Second troop, rally here!" *"Par ici, les lanciers!"* Major Tallmadge, head high under his white-crested helmet, loomed through the dark. He called, "Ledyard! Captain Ledyard, report!"

"Here, Major," shouted Grant as Tallmadge reined in. "God, but this was a close-run thing."

"This is fine work, Ledyard, the whole thing. But how in God's name did you get wind of it?" Tallmadge dismounted and tipped back his helmet to wipe his forehead.

"Someone came across the Sound," said Grant cautiously. "All the way from Manhattan."

Tallmadge looked keenly at Grant, then raised his hand to his helmet as though in salute. "The best of us all," he said slowly. "I hope some day the country can know about him." He glanced down the road. "And here come the lancers." A hint of a smile was in his voice as he said, *"Now* what do you think of the French, Ledyard?"

"I'll serve with them anytime they'll have me." He called over the slap-slap of hoofs, *"Holà,* Captain d'Ostel!"

A figure detached itself from the little column, dismounted. "At your service," said d'Ostel.

"Major, the Chevalier d'Ostel. The army can thank him and his men for saving the gold."

As Tallmadge shook his hand, d'Ostel protested, *"Du tout.* One merely made arrangements, one considered measures, most of which would have been useless without the aid — "

Tallmadge laughed. "If you're going to quarrel about credit, I'll overrule you both and take it for myself. You're wounded, Captain?"

"A blow on the head, which now aches like forty thousand devils and a nibble on the shoulder which bled much and hurt little." He drew himself up, bowed to Tallmadge. "With your permission, *mon commandant,* I return to the house. I wish to reassure myself about the young ladies."

"Was Polly with you through all this!" exclaimed Tallmadge.

"There was no other way. We kept her and Rosa Hollis in shelter as best we could."

"Rosa Hollis, too?" exclaimed Tallmadge. "You know, not a half mile from here, my patrols rode right over Jethro Hollis and that niece of his. And when I came up, damned if he didn't snap a pistol at me and try to get away."

Grant slapped his leg. "Hollis! Major — he's still with you?"

"Of course. I don't understand it, but I couldn't take the time to question him then. He's under guard back there with the girl."

Grant gave a shout of relief. "Then you've got it — once and for all."

"I've got him. What do you mean by 'it'?"

"The leak to the British. It's been Hollis all the time, Hollis and Laurel. With a good many helpers, of course."

"What?" Tallmadge's voice was sharp. "Jethro Hollis? Can't be!"

"Can't be anything else. He brought the men here today. Laurel was with him and shot at Sammis's stableboy when he tried to break away. I saw that. There isn't a doubt. Rosa, Hollis's daughter, is here too, but I know she had nothing to do with it."

Tallmadge's voice snapped out and a dragoon materialized out of the night. "To Captain Crawford. Treble the guard about that pair we picked up. He'll be personally answerable to me for them." The dragoon vanished and Tallmadge went on in a lower tone, "Hollis! Well, the Commander will know how to handle them both, uncle and niece. Also, he'll know how to handle you and d'Ostel. That part of my report ought to give him a lot of pleasure. Now let's go to the house."

Lamps glowed all through the lower floor and shimmered from upper windows. The improvised loopholes showed raggedly. A French voice yelled in triumph that the last of the gold boxes had been recovered. Tallmadge entered, and Grant saw his eyes darting right and left as a dozen signs told him the story of the fight. In the room to the right of the door, several bodies lay, covered with dragoon or lancer cloaks. The major's face tightened and his hand went to his visor again. "And, oh, before I forget it, I want to have a word with d'Ostel." He strode off down the corridor calling for the chevalier.

A door at Grant's right, which had been partially masked by Tallmadge's broad shoulders, swung gently open and Polly held out her hands to Grant. "Is it really over?" she whispered.

Grant caught her hands. "Really over. I'd have come to you before but —"

"I know. You were with Major Tallmadge. He saw me when I opened the door. That's why he wanted to talk to d'Ostel so suddenly."

Polly slipped her arm through his. "Let's go into the little room beyond the kitchen. I nearly tripped up that last lancer who edged past us." She led him down the corridor and into the little room. "This seems so odd, Grant. For once there's nobody calling for us, nothing that we have to do, nothing to pull us apart." She smoothed back her dark hair. "Do you know what I was thinking while Rosa and I were smoking the glasses? I kept thinking of that burned house across from the Oxbow. I could fix that up so you'd never know anything had happened to it and there's a lovely place for a garden."

Grant laughed happily. "You were thinking of all that? And you'd like to live in Fairfield?"

"Well," said Polly slowly, "it's a pretty town and besides it's very close to a rather nice man I know."

Grant narrowed his eyes. "You mean right away? I don't know that Tallmadge would approve of your being so close to the coast just yet."

Polly set her chin. "Oh, he'll approve. We'll ask him. Do go and find him, Grant."

Grant left the room, stepped out onto the drive where he found Tallmadge giving a few last orders to some dragoons. The major looked around. "That you, Ledyard? All quiet out here. It seems as though our late enemies are still running." He drew Grant aside. "Does the Hollis girl know we've got her father and her cousin?"

"She must guess. This is going to be very hard on her, Major."

"Can't be helped. I've sent them both on to the Commander with a letter recommending that Hollis be sent to the Simsbury prison. The girl's different. I'm suggesting that we just send her back to the British lines under a flag of truce. She can't do us any more harm." He drew a deep breath. "So we're at peace — for the moment. Let's go in and have a drink. Where's your young lady?"

"Polly's waiting in that little room off the kitchen. She's got something she wants to ask you."

"Ask me?" said Tallmadge. "I hope I can tell her what she wants to know."

In the room off the kitchen he greeted Polly warmly, thanked her for all that she had done. Then drawing two bottles out from under his coat, he said, "Here we are. Rum for us, wine for the ladies. I've sent word for Miss Hollis to join us with d'Ostel."

Tallmadge uncorked the bottles, pouring wine and rum. He turned to Polly, handing her a glass, "There's something you wanted to ask me?"

"Yes," said Polly. "It's about — well — Grant knows of a house in Fairfield that he wants to fix up for us. You won't mind, will you? I'm sure it's safe for me there now."

"Fairfield?" Tallmadge raised his eyebrows. "Yes, it'd be safe enough I'd say, now that the leak has been stopped. But you wouldn't like it there, my dear."

"Why not?" cried Polly, surprised.

"For a number of reasons. For one thing — " he broke off, as Rosa entered the room, pale but composed; d'Ostel, a lancer's jacket buttoned over his bandages followed, pulled out a chair for her. "Do we interrupt?" asked the chevalier.

"By no means," said Tallmadge blandly. "You may even be able to confirm my opinion that Miss Morgan would not like Fairfield."

"I do not understand," said d'Ostel frowning.

257

"Patience," smiled Tallmadge. "The chief reason is that she'd be too far from that dragoon captain across from me."

"Too far from me?" echoed Grant. "I've got to be there. How about my work?"

"Winter's coming. Both armies will be idle till spring. There'll be no need to travel over that certain road we all know."

"I'm going back to regimental duty, you mean?" asked Grant. "Then, Polly, you'll have to find a house near Northcastle."

Tallmadge shook his head. "Still too far. Chevalier, what would you say about an American aide at Lebanon?"

D'Ostel, who had been sitting silently between Polly and Rosa, started. "An American aide at Lebanon? Ah, one may see its advantages."

"Then, my dear," Tallmadge bowed to Polly, "you'd better turn your mind to a house or tent at Lebanon. Yes. Ledyard. The Commander's orders. I have them in my kit"

D'Ostel sprang to his feet. "But I find this delightful. It is the Legion of Lauzun that will be content. My own little devils will take further heart at the presence of the lady of the smoked glass. Or, one should say, the ladies of the smoked glass, since I assume that Mademoiselle Rosa will go too."

Rosa gave a little gasp. "I? I hadn't thought — there's no future for me to look to."

Polly laid her hand over Rosa's. "If you want to go back to the Aspetuck, I know there'll be an escort for you and a way of letting people know what you did for us."

Rosa shook her head, eyes downcast. "No — I can't go back there, knowing what I do and people remembering who I am. But then, I guess I'll have to. There's Aunt Ann, all alone."

"No, no," urged Polly. "If you don't want to go back there, bring your Aunt Ann along with you to Lebanon."

D'Ostel said earnestly. "The Legion would take that as an honor, mademoiselle. I speak in the name of the Duc de Lauzun who will extend to you and madame, your aunt, his personal protection."

"There!" cried Polly. "Say you'll come."

Rosa nodded silently, but her eyes thanked Polly and d'Ostel.

Grant raised his glass. "Then I drink to a pleasant Franco-American winter at Lebanon."

"Eh? *Quoi?*" cried d'Ostel. "One drinks a health? Yes, to that one I raise my glass. But then may I propose one that none of us here should forget. Ah, my glass is high and my heart with it as I drink to one about whom my good friend Ledyard had hinted, and to whom we owe the fact that we sit here, alive and victorious. You guess the man, Major Tallmadge? Yes, that timid man and his secret road!"

Beverly Robinson House

Sugar Loaf
Mountain

Danb̶

North Salem

Peekskill

Salem

CROTON RIVER

Stony Point

Ridgefi̶

Northcastle

Vulture

Jeller's Point

Colonel Jameson's
Headquarters

W E S T C H E S T E R
C O U N T Y

F A I R F I E L D
C O U N T Y

New

Tarrytown

York

Stamford

Tappan

White Plains

Port
Chester

Lon̶
Po̶

Mamaroneck

L O N G

Lloyd Poin̶

New Jersey

Hempstead
Harbor

Oyster
Bay

Col̶
Spri̶
Harb̶

North or Hudson River

Manhattan I.

Raynham Hall

Whitestone

Flushing

New
York

Onderdonck's Inn

Avon

Brooklyn

Staten
Island

Coenties Slip
(Grant cast
ashore here)

Jamaica

Hempstead

The Narrows

Jamaica
Bay

Gre̶